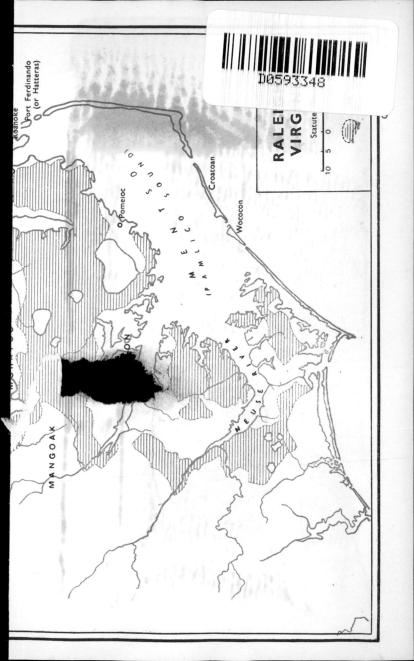

RALEIGH

and the

British Empire

is one of the volumes
in the
TEACH YOURSELF HISTORY
LIBRARY

Teach Yourself History

VOLUMES READY OR IN PREPARATION

RALEIGH

and the

British Empire

by
DAVID B. QUINN

Andrew Geddes and John Rankin
Professor of Modern History
in the University Of Liverpool

THE ENGLISH UNIVERSITIES PRESS LTD
102, Newgate Street
LONDON, E.C.1

FIRST PRINTED OCTOBER 1947
NEW EDITION (RE-SET) 1962

PRINTED IN GREAT BRITAIN FOR THE ENGLISH UNIVERSITIES PRESS, LTD
LONDON, BY ELLIOTT BROS. AND YEOMAN LTD., LIVERPOOL

A General Introduction to the Series

THIS series has been undertaken in the conviction that there can be no subject of study more important than history. Great as have been the conquests of natural science in our time —such that many think of ours as a scientific age *par excellence*—it is even more urgent and necessary that advances should be made in the social sciences, if we are to gain control of the forces of nature loosed upon us. The bed out of which all the social sciences spring is history; there they find, in greater or lesser degree, subject-matter and material, verification or contradiction.

There is no end to what we can learn from history, if only we will, for it is coterminous with life. Its special field is the life of man in society, and at every point we can learn vicariously from the experience of others before us in history.

To take one point only—the understanding of politics: how can we hope to understand the world of affairs around us if we do not know how it came to be what it is? How to understand Germany, or Soviet Russia, or the United States —or ourselves, without knowing something of their history?

There is no subject that is more useful, or indeed indispensable.

Some evidence of the growing awareness of this may be seen in the immense increase in the interest of the reading public in history, and the much larger place the subject has come to take in education in our time.

This series has been planned to meet the needs and demands of a very wide public and of education—they are indeed the same. I am convinced that the most congenial, as well as the most concrete and practical, approach to history is the biographical, through the lives of the great men whose actions have been so much part of history, and whose careers in turn have been so moulded and formed by events.

The key idea of this series, and what distinguishes it from any other that has appeared, is the intention by way of a biography of a great man to open up a significant historical theme; for example, Cromwell and the Puritan Revolution, or Lenin and the Russian Revolution.

My hope is, in the end, as the series fills out and completes itself, by a sufficient number of biographies to cover whole periods and subjects in that way. To give you the history of the United States, for example, or the British Empire or France, via a number of biographies of their leading historical figures.

That should be something new, as well as convenient and practical, in education.

I need hardly say that I am a strong believer in people with good academic standards writing once more for the general reading public, and of the public being given the best that the universities can provide. From this point of view this series is intended to bring the university into the homes of the people.

A. L. ROWSE.

ALL SOULS COLLEGE,
    OXFORD.

Contents

Illustrations

Introduction

THE greatest theme of modern history is the impact of the western European peoples on the world overseas and the effects which imperialism had on their own society. In all the aspects of this movement, even though a late-comer to colonial enterprise, Britain played an outstanding part, whether in commerce, colonization, the exploitation of overseas peoples or in the exchange of ideas. Each phase of her imperial activity was the result of social and economic changes inside the British Isles, and was the work of very many men striving for power and profits, while transforming the ways of living of non-Europeans in the process. To ascribe to any individual too large a share in empire-building would be misleading. Imperialism is always an expression of social forces and not, primarily, of individual initiative. It is, therefore, as a representative figure, an originating rather than a dominating one, that Sir Walter Raleigh should be regarded in the history of the beginnings of British overseas enterprise.

Sir Walter Raleigh has always attracted biographers. His complex, many-sided character and interests, and the many points at which he affected the life of his own time, have offered a challenge to successive generations. Yet we still lack a single complete and convincing picture of all his activities. It is because he had originality and a zest for discovery, and applied them to the initiation of British settlements in North America, that he has been chosen here to exemplify and illustrate a whole social movement. Other aspects of his career are only briefly sketched. This book does not attempt, therefore, a complete biography.

Raleigh's life extended through the experiments of Elizabethan pioneers to the threshold of an age of significant imperial achievement. His own overseas interests were mainly concentrated on the earliest attempts to establish colonies of Englishmen outside the British Isles. He was only slightly concerned with the building up of commerce with Russia, Africa, the Levant and the East Indies—an essential part of British mercantile imperialism. Consequently, the illustration of early overseas expansion from Raleigh's own ideas and activities must necessarily be incomplete and partial. Its justification is the important place which colonization occupies in the history of the British Empire.

It is more usual for pioneers to point the way to success than to attain it for themselves. Raleigh's life is, indeed, a record of successive failures. As was the case with many of his contemporaries, his ideas and aims outstripped the social means available for their achievement. It is probably true, after we discount all the accidents and mistakes which occurred, that the resources of Elizabethan England were scarcely adequate for successful overseas colonization. While not all Raleigh's abilities could make them so, his experiments helped to lay foundations on which the earliest British overseas colony—and a later republic—could be established.

Foreword

SIR Walter Raleigh continues to interest the twentieth century. As a man of many contradictions, concerned intimately with his own predicament, he has the appeal today that he had for some of his contemporaries as a man peculiarly self-conscious. 'Brave knowing, yet ignorant Rauleigh', said one of them, 'knowing too much how to know thyself; yet ignorant in bestowing too little on others'. He was aware at the last of the harm that the egotistical side of his self-absorption had done him. 'I never travailed after men's opinions when I might have made the best use of them', he admitted in *The Historie of the World* towards the end of his life. We know him now as the courtier better than we did, through Walter Oakeshott's *The Queen and the Poet* (1960). There we see him carrying on his verse courtship of Queen Elizabeth, his 'twelve years' war' as he was to call it: first the young man clinging to the skirts of the court, willing to serve but pleading for the perquisites to enable him to do so; then the lover, gratified with gold if not with passion, continuing a campaign of courtly flattery with fine words, behind which were, characteristically, both a core of feeling and a flavour of satire; next the declining, jealous rival, rejecting Essex, mistrusting his mistress, hoping still for the turn of the Queen's favour; at last (1592) the distressed, discarded favourite, writing his haunted lines to his Cynthia (as he called the Queen):

> Twelve years entire I wasted in this war
> Twelve years of my most happy younger days
> But I in them, and they now wasted are
> Of all which past, the sorrow only stays.

After the Queen broke with him over his marriage he pulled himself back to prominence at Court, after some five years, but only at a somewhat lower level, respected and distrusted at the same time by Elizabeth and by her advisers, allowed to remain on the margin of the innermost governing group. During his disgrace he and his friends won for themselves the label of 'atheists', which Catholic propagandists endeavoured to fasten to them firmly. Ernest A. Strathmann's *Sir Walter Ralegh. A Study in Elizabethan Skepticism* (1951) examined his underlying attitudes about religion and philosophy, showing him to be basically orthodox in belief but open-minded and critical of established ways of thought, an enemy of the old medieval world order that hung on in so much Elizabethan thinking, a pillar of the new, quasi-scientific enlightenment with which we associate Sir Francis Bacon's name. Yet the attacks on him had some effect. His reputed views, together with his ruthless treatment of his adversaries, led him to be thought capable of anything, a dangerous man. He lay open to slander, intrigue and destruction at the hands of his rivals at the opening of a new reign.

Yet his range was remarkable. Man of action and inspirer of action in others (as this little book shows in some detail); businessman (grasping monopolist and unscrupulous privateer at times); ingenious politician (capable of devious intrigues); statesman (whose advice when asked was often wise, but who had no gift for sharing responsibility with others); administrator (but allowed his way only in Cornwall and the Channel Islands); amateur scientist and sponsor of scientific experiments by others; sceptical observer of the past and of his own times—these are only a few of his roles. We could still do with more knowledge of some of them. Willard M. Wallace, *Sir Walter Raleigh* (1959), has more detail on a number of them than most recent biographies. Agnes M. C. Latham has been able to tell us (in *Essays and Studies by Members of the English Association*, 1951) more than we have known about his search for a gold-mine in his last voyage. She and Pierre Lefranc have (in *Etudes anglaises*, 1956) also modified our views about such elementary biographical facts as the date of his birth and the circumstances of his marriage. It has proved possible to make a few other small corrections to this edition. But the man is still something of a myth. The prisoner in the Tower, the scapegoat, the anti-Spanish hero so stamped one image of himself on the seventeenth century that the bright Elizabethan still casts his shadow on the Stuarts.

DAVID B. QUINN

LIVERPOOL, SEPTEMBER 1961

Chapter One

Beginnings

ABOUT 1554—for a precise birth-date has yet to be found for him—Walter Raleigh was born, the fourth son of Walter Raleigh of Fardel, near Plymouth. His father was one of the lesser Devon gentry, well connected but poor. Walter was born at Hayes Barton, a few miles from Budleigh Salterton Bay, to which his father had moved over twenty years before. His mother, Katherine Champernoun, was a member of another family of Devonshire gentry. She had married Otho Gilbert of Compton and, after his death in 1547, had become the third wife of the elder Walter Raleigh. She was the mother of five men, Sir John, Sir Humphrey and Adrian Gilbert, and Sir Walter and Sir Carew Raleigh, all actively associated in English overseas expansion.

Raleigh was born at a significant time. For nearly a century successive English governments, under Yorkist and Tudor kings, had been endeavouring to build a compact and centralized state out of the broken-down feudalism of the fifteenth century. It was only under Henry VIII that northern England, Wales and the Welsh marches were brought in any effective sense under the control of the central government, and for some generations local particularism was still a factor of importance in the state. Only after 1534 had a beginning been made in establishing an effective English administration in Ireland, which had to be extended by continuous wars in the latter part of the century towards complete domination of the island. Scotland, in spite of Tudor plans for her subjugation, was to remain a separate and disturbing influence on the northern borders until the union of the crowns in 1603. The handing back of Boulogne to France in 1550 left only the Calais bridgehead, very soon to be lost, as a reminder of the medieval continental empire. Mid-sixteenth-century England was thus a small state, covering little more than half the British Isles and possessing only Calais and the Channel Islands outside them.

Inside this little state of some four million people, affairs were in a critical stage. The first Tudors had decapitated the feudal rivals of the monarchy, and had used vigorous civil servants and a subservient Parliament to curb the territorial power of the nobility. Henry VIII, with equal thoroughness, had cut the ties which bound England to the international church, and by despoiling the monks, had brought to the monarchy resources in money and land which made England a European power to be reckoned with. The changes in the balance of property in the country had been accompanied by religious dissension; the schismatic orthodoxy of Henry VIII's last years was giving place to radical Protestant experiments under the boy-king Edward VI. These, in turn, were to lead to the reaction towards Roman Catholicism under Mary and to the compromise Protestantism of the Elizabethan settlement. Until this see-saw of state-inspired religious belief could find some level, the international position of England remained in jeopardy, and she was afflicted with civil dissensions which threatened to undo the unifying work of the early Tudors.

Social relationships were also in a state of flux. The early Tudor kings had aimed at establishing something of an equilibrium in the state. Over against the territorial power of the feudal magnates they had tried to encourage and build up the middle strata of society. A stable government appealed strongly to the merchants and, until after the defeat of the Spanish *armada*, the *bourgeoisie* remained strong supporters of Tudor centralism. The gentry were, in most areas, glad to be freed by an over-riding state authority from the protective but inhibiting embrace of the feudal nobility. They were kept loyal to the state by the delegation of local powers, by the pickings of monastic lands and by the growth of the prestige of the commons' house in Parliament. Out of the minor Churchmen, estate officials, merchants and gentry the Tudors built a bureaucracy, carefully enriching and ennobling its ablest members to give them a material and hereditary interest in the continuance of the dynasty.

The stability of the Tudor state was less firmly grounded than is often believed. It had to improvise repeatedly in its dealings with the middle-classes, for traders and gentlemen tended to develop demands for power as well as perquisites, which were to lead, at the end of the century, to those Parliamentary challenges to monarchical power which presaged the middle-class revolution of the seventeenth century. Consequently, there is frequent conflict and intrigue beneath the surface, with the government trying to keep the middle-classes as a whole reasonably loyal by playing off various groups against each other. Below the propertied classes, too, Tudor England had a smouldering social problem. Enclosures, the breaking down of feudal ties and households, fluctuations in trade, changes in currency values, prices and rents, as well as a certain rise in population, brought successive crises to many of the small farmers, agricultural labourers and town workers. Misery and hunger created a spectre of peasant and town revolts, which threatened the newly enriched elements in the middle classes. The Tudor state had to build up organs of repression against its lower classes, as well as to ameliorate

4

the worst aspects of poverty. The creation of employment by warfare on land and sea seemed to some in the latter part of the century a legitimate programme for keeping social discontent within limits.

English prosperity depended on two main economic factors—an expanding export trade and the development of domestic agriculture. The confiscation of monastic lands enriched some of the new men by speculation, but many more by the more efficient exploitation of the land. Land was the only stable investment available for most people with capital to spare, and, with trade expansion and the freeing of land from the dead hand of the Church, land prices rose. Merchants, especially goldsmiths—the bankers of the period—government officials and country gentlemen, managed to attain wealth and influence when they had business initiative; while poor tenants had their rents pushed up and got poorer, and the less efficient, or more feudally-minded, landowners went to the wall.

The development of merchant capital during the years 1480-1550 was, in spite of periodic slumps in trade, remarkably rapid. The main reason was a boom in exports of unfinished cloth, which more than doubled in the first half of the new century. Up to 1550 the merchants, and all the industrial and agricultural groups dependent on the cloth industry, were doing increasingly well. But after 1550 there was a startling change. There were two catastrophic slumps and extensive cuts in average cloth exports during the next twenty-five years. This increased social friction inside the country, but it also forced merchants and industrialists to experiment with new products for sale in new markets overseas. They were helped, though slowly, by the import of bullion from extra-European lands, which added to the available mobile capital, and by the consequent price increases. In the attempt to make new lines of marketable goods, England began her first industrial revolution, which transformed certain sections of her economy in the period down to 1640. In the search for new markets and sources of supply, Englishmen began to explore new seas and lands far outside the old orbit of medieval trade, as well as to plunder the more successful overseas powers. It was largely by these means that a measure of economic advance was achieved in the latter part of the sixteenth century.

At the time of Raleigh's birth, Tudor England was passing through what, perhaps, was its greatest crisis. The dominating personality of Henry VIII had gone, leaving a boy at the head of the state. The bureaucracy was left to rule the country. They quarrelled among themselves over the rich spoils left in their hands, and faction let loose a flood of anarchy. The religious orientation of the country was not yet determined, and Protestant experiments, under Somerset and Northumberland, allowed conservative forces to develop a new drive towards feudal reaction. The great trade slumps, aggravated by currency inflation and exploited by conservative feudalists, drove the poor countrymen to rise in the bitterest revolts of the century. It seemed that the Tudor state might dissolve in anarchy. Though the death of Edward was followed by Northumberland's mad bid to make Lady Jane Grey queen, the capacity of Mary and her advisers somehow saved the state. Mary, even if she restored the old Church (though not the monastic lands), got control of the reins of administration and pulled the machinery of government into shape, but her foreign husband and her disastrous foreign entanglements enabled Elizabeth to reverse her religious and foreign policy while continuing sound administration.

In these critical years of the mid-century, Walter Raleigh grew up. We know nothing of his boyhood in south Devon. His parents' allegiance to the unpopular Protestant side brought them into danger for a time, but their extensive connexions amongst the county gentry saved them from harm, and with the accession of Elizabeth they settled down to a modest prosperity. It is not known where Raleigh went to school, but once he was free of it he looked for action not study. The French wars beckoned. By the spring of 1569 he had slipped away, soon followed by some older friends and relations from Devonshire who volunteered to fight on the Huguenot side in the interminable religious wars. It is uncertain how much time he spent in France, but he was glad in the end to return and settle down as a student at Oxford. He was at Oriel College in 1572 and is likely to have stayed until 1574. He left without a degree and went on to finish his education as a gentleman, and was entered first at Lyon's Inn, one of the Inns of Chancery, and later, in February 1575, at the Middle Temple. In the spring of 1576 he contributed, as 'Walter Rawley of the Middle Temple,' commendatory verses to George Gascoigne's poem, *The Steele Glas*. Later, Raleigh was living at Islington with some footing at Court and, evidently, with something of an income, for in December 1577 he had to bail out two of his servants who had got embroiled with the watch. This is almost all that is known about his adolescence.

By 1578 Walter Raleigh was at least six feet tall, well-made, straight and commanding. His face was long, and his bold chin was not yet bearded, though he may already have worn a tuft and moustache. His nose was pronounced but regular, and his forehead high, though obscured by dark curling hair. Later his hair receded and he grew a beard, which in his middle-age he wore long and pointed. He always retained a strong Devonshire accent. He loved fine clothes and jewels, and had a good deal of personal vanity.

Only the vaguest memories of his youth have come down to us. An omnivorous reader, he may have distinguished himself in oratory and philosophy as an undergraduate, though he did not take a degree. As a young but studious soldier of fortune, he acquired an enduring interest in strategy and tactics. While his admission to the Middle Temple did not necessarily imply any serious study of law, some of his later writings suggest that he had interests in jurisprudence. The Inns of Court were, in a real sense, the London University of the sixteenth century, and he lived there in a more mature student society than at Oxford and in contact with literature and intellect. His Gascoigne verses are the earliest evidence of his interest in verse-making —few intelligent contemporaries of his did not dabble in this amusement—but he was to become, among the rest, a serious poet. Our knowledge of his earliest contacts at Court is too amorphous to show him as anything more than one of some fifteen hundred officials, courtiers, servants and hangers-on. It seems probable from later indications that he was reasonably dissolute, and the violent temper which he shared with his half-brother, Sir Humphrey Gilbert, involved him in quarrels. His considerable intellectual powers were being sharpened in this

London society; his ambitions were being seriously focused towards gaining advancement and, possibly, wealth and power.

Thus far Walter Raleigh's story had been, for the younger son of a poor but well-connected country gentleman, a very ordinary one indeed. Professor Tawney,[1] in discussing the rise of the class of Tudor gentry, speaks of 'the ruthlessness of the English family system which sacrificed the individual to the institution and, if it did not drown all the kittens but one, threw all but one into the water, pouring the martyrs of that prudent egotism, their younger sons, not only into the learned professions, but into armies, English and foreign, exploration and colonization, and every branch of business enterprise.' The younger sons of landowning families were a prominent phenomenon of the Elizabethan age: like the unemployed—the able-bodied beggars—they were considered to be a social problem. In most cases the whole, or by far the larger part, of the family estate was earmarked for the eldest son; the old vast feudal households to which such young men had formerly attached themselves were dying out; the monastic life, to which some had been consigned, had been swept away so that, as a writer complained in 1571, 'the excessive expense, both in diet and apparel, maketh that men which

[1] R. H. Tawney, 'The rise of the gentry,' in *Economic History Review*, XI, 319–41.

have but small portions cannot maintain themselves in the emulation of this world with like countenance as the grounded rich can do.' All that a parent like the elder Walter Raleigh could do for one of his younger sons was to give him something of an education at one of the universities and at the finishing school of the Inns of Court and modestly subsidize him until he should have found his own feet.

Many of these young men were drawn to the Court. There, if they had suitable introductions and connexions, they could get fed and entertained. By dint of looks or personality, or application or sharp practice, they might obtain employment, perquisites and even the great prize—notice from the Queen herself. It was while Raleigh was looking around the town and the Court, enjoying himself, probably beginning to worry about his future and discussing ways of winning money or fame, that he became involved, in 1578, with his half-brother, Sir Humphrey Gilbert, in planning the establishment of English colonies in America. He was, to begin with, a very junior partner in an imperfectly thought-out enterprise, but the overseas world gradually came to fill a larger part of his thoughts and to inspire him to action on his own account.

Chapter Two

New Worlds

IN 1578 England had not a single foothold outside Europe, even though the most remarkable achievement of fifteenth- and early sixteenth-century Europe and been to open up the way to, and begin the exploitation of, vast territories in Africa, Asia and America hitherto untouched by European civilization. The pioneer colonial powers were Portugal and Spain. Less than sixty years after Columbus's first discoveries, Spain dominated the principal Caribbean islands, Mexico, Central America, Peru and many other parts of South America. She had laid claim to the whole of the gradually unfolding American continent, and from it prodigious streams of silver were flowing to transform European economy.

Portugal had sailed more slowly into world dominion. A hundred years of discovery and trading had brought her soldiers and merchants gradually down the west coast of Africa and, at the very end of the fifteenth century, into the Indian Ocean. In another fifty years Portugal, with posts throughout the East Indies, had become the chief supplier of spices, silks and

12

jewels to a still astonished Europe, while across
the Atlantic she was gradually building up a
colony in Brazil. Through Iberian agency,
Europe had burst into new worlds, where skill
in ship-construction and navigation, gunpowder,
powers of organization for business or government, cruelty, cunning and daring enterprise
could apparently overcome all obstacles to
wealth and power.

This astonishing revolution had been made
possible by many economic, social and political
factors. Chief among them was the development
of European industry. In Italy, in the Netherlands and in Spain itself industrial centres had
developed, capable of supplying not only European demands but also new markets overseas.
Out of the profits of industry and trade bankers
in Italy and Germany had been able to accumulate sufficient capital resources to finance the
expensive initial overseas ventures. The consolidation of certain European states brought
into being the centralized authority and the
machinery for levying taxation necessary to
enable the rulers of Portugal, Castile and
Aragon to become the instruments of trading
and financial interests which sought super-profits
from new discoveries and markets. Technical
developments, largely associated with industrial
and social changes, made it possible for men to
sail abroad in seaworthy vessels and with relatively effective firearms. Intellectual speculation

13

about the outside world was freeing itself from medieval prohibitions. Training in the administration of centralized European states paved the way for successful experiments in governing overseas territories.

In Africa and Asia, Portugal was concerned with setting up trading bases rather than with territorial aggrandizement or colonization. In America, the Spaniards, confronted mainly with a sparse population of mobile, barbarian peoples, had to resort to European settlement on a considerable scale so as to exploit the resources of the new continent. As a result of the efflux of settlers to America, an important urban civilization was springing up there, with a rural society of large European landowners exploiting in servitude the native occupants of the land. African slaves were imported in considerable numbers to overcome the deficiencies of native labour on the land and in the mines. The Spanish-American towns were far apart, the agricultural land the settlers occupied being only a tiny fraction of the whole, but over them all was built a tight structure of royal administration and trade monopoly. Yet not all the vast energy of the sixteenth-century Spaniards and their backers and assistants from other lands could even begin to occupy the whole American continent. North America, apart from a certain filtration outwards from Mexico, remained untouched.

Spain and Portugal had endeavoured to close the doors behind them. To France, to England and to all other European aspirants to empire they had said, 'You can have no passage here.' They had reinforced their monopoly by treaties and by papal sanctions, yet they could never have maintained it for long but for the initial weakness of their possible competitors and for the astonishing speed and luck which brought them so much wealth from both East and West that they were rapidly able to make themselves strong. It was only in the last thirty years of the century that their monopoly began to be seriously challenged. From books, travellers' tales, the adventures of a few explorers and pirates, and from second-hand trading contacts, other Europeans learned something of the new lands. For the most part they could not approach them or exploit their riches directly.

Englishmen, and sailors of other nations sponsored by them, had a place in the early history of overseas discovery. Between 1480 and 1491, it seems, Bristol seamen found the 'Isle of Brasil' (Newfoundland?) when in search of new fishing grounds. Then, in 1496, John Cabot received his patent from Henry VII to discover and conquer for the English realm unknown lands beyond the seas, and sailed in 1497 to make a fully authenticated landfall on the North American coast, either at Newfoundland or Nova Scotia. He called attention to the swarming fish of the Newfoundland Banks and, believing that he had found the outlying coast of Asia, sailed again in 1498 to trade with China. His voyage was a disappointment. He may himself have been lost, after some considerable exploration of the American coast had shown that this land was not Cathay. The survivors cannot have brought home very encouraging reports. His work was followed up between 1501 and 1505 by syndicates of Bristol merchants and Azorean Portuguese, who did a little trade with the American Indians, but the difficulties of the passage and the discovery only of primitive peoples with little to exchange led to the dropping of the ventures. Sebastian Cabot did, apparently, make a voyage in 1508–9 in search of a north-west passage round North America to Asia, but he achieved nothing except the establishment of a pertinacious myth.

English merchants, on whose willingness to pay for expeditions the exploitation of these American discoveries depended, were too much concerned in building up the cloth trade to bother about what appeared to be a barren continent on the other side of the Atlantic. Only when there was a slump in trade were they prepared to make any investments in western exploration. During a trade depression, a large-scale project for selling English cloth in America and attempting to open a westward route to Asia was sponsored by the King in 1521, and received

some support from the London merchants. It
fell through when the risks of loss were seen to
be considerable and when, in any case, trade
began to revive. In 1527 and 1536 there were
exploratory voyages along parts of the American
coast; while from 1527 to the end of the reign
of Henry VIII, Robert Thorne and Roger
Barlow were unsuccessfully urging the government to take in hand the discovery and development of a short sea passage through northerly
waters to the rich markets of Asia. The only
concrete achievement in western waters before
1550 was some English participation in the Newfoundland cod-fisheries, which, however, were
mainly being exploited by Portuguese, Spanish
and French Basque, Norman and Breton fishermen. After 1550 there was a change in outlook.
The collapse of the cloth trade provided an
incentive to search for new markets, even in
apparently unlikely directions. This was almost
immediately responsible for the opening-up of a
sea-borne trade with Russia by a company
formed to discover a sea-passage to Asia. It led
also, though much more slowly, to greater
interest in the possibilities of North America.

These spasmodic English efforts to follow up
the pioneer discoveries all took place outside the
sphere of effective Spanish and Portuguese
colonial activity. Until after 1558, the English
government gave no encouragement to sailors or
merchants to encroach directly on the Spanish

monopoly. Merchants had to be content to send their goods to America through Spanish channels, and to receive American products at second-hand from Spain or the Netherlands. So far as the Portuguese monopoly was concerned, neither governments nor merchants were so scrupulous. The gold and ivory of West Africa were enticing a few English merchants into the Portuguese area as early as 1480–8, but it was not until 1530 that William Hawkins began to establish something like a regular trade with Guinea and Brazil, and he was followed by a few others. In this area, too, the turn of the century marked the beginning of a new era. From 1551 a regular traffic was maintained with the Atlantic coast of Morocco, and from 1553 onwards English merchants made great efforts against Portuguese resistance, but with some success, to build up a steady trade with West Africa. The increase in sea-borne trade and the development of shipping in western Europe produced a considerable increase in piracy and privateering. The French were the pioneers in the plunder of Spanish and Portuguese vessels coming from the colonies, but Englishmen too were beginning to acquire clandestinely a little of the wealth which was flowing into Europe from overseas.

Throughout Elizabeth's reign, English merchants were pushing farther and farther afield in their trading contacts in the old world. They were trying to trade overland with Asia—by way of Russia, Persia and the Levant. They were penetrating in strength into the Baltic and the Mediterranean. At the end of the century, after a long and costly apprenticeship, they broke through the Portuguese monopoly by establishing direct contact by sea with the East Indies, on the basis of which an English trading empire in the East was built up in the seventeenth century.

The definite breach between England and Catholic Europe which Elizabeth's accession marked involved a loss of respect by Englishmen for the old sanctions by which the Spanish monopoly was guarded. Although Elizabeth did her best to remain on peaceable terms with Philip II, her subjects were allowed an appreciable amount of licence and, indeed, as piracy and illict trade became a vested interest in the south-western ports, she was not able wholly to prevent infringements of Spanish privileges. In her early years, John Hawkins made a daring attempt to prise open the American monopoly by selling negro slaves to the Spanish colonists in the Caribbean.

His success in 1562-3 induced the Queen to invest in his second venture of 1563-4, and it appeared that Spain might allow some limited trade in negroes. But a contrary decision was made, the third expedition was attacked at San Juan de Ulua, and Hawkins limped home in 1569 after heavy losses. The first of a series of

crises in the colonial relations of the two countries, this coincided with a conflict on domestic
matters, lasting from 1568 to 1573. Philip intervened to aid a rebellion and a series of plots
against Elizabeth, while she impounded bullion
on its way to the Netherlands, allowed 'volunteers' to aid the insurgent Dutch and released
privateers to prey on Spanish shipping. Though
trade relations were patched up in 1573, they
were never again really peaceful.

The crisis had a special overseas significance.
From 1570, with or without royal connivance,
the piratically-inclined south-western gentry
maintained constant attacks on Spanish treasure-
fleets and colonial settlements. Drake was the
leading figure in much of this. His plan in 1572
was to seize the Isthmus of Panama, in order to
intercept the silver and gold coming up the
Pacific coast for trans-shipment to Europe. He
had some success in his landing on the mainland
of Central America in 1572–3, and was soon
followed by other marauding parties. The more
ambitious plan of occupying the isthmus and
installing a permanent garrison there, thus
cutting the Spanish empire in two, was not
attempted.

Although after 1569 seamen and merchants
and some prominent officials at Court wished the
government to take the risk of attempting to
challenge the Spanish monopoly directly, the
Queen and her advisers were too realistic to risk

all by throwing the small resources of the island kingdom against the wealth of the Iberian empires. Yet the idea was gaining ground that Englishmen should seize and occupy overseas territories of their own, if not within the areas more or less effectively occupied by the Spaniards and Portuguese, then outside them. A new and striking concept, derived from geographical theorists, was that of settling the South Pacific continent, known as *Terra Australis Incognita*, which was presumed to exist to the west and north-west of the Strait of Magellan. An English expedition in search of this undiscovered continent was projected by a group of Devonshire and Cornish gentlemen, headed by Raleigh's cousin, Richard Grenville, and including his uncle, Sir Arthur Champernoun. A draft patent from the Crown authorizing the scheme was prepared but not sealed, and the scheme dropped, though it appeared again as one of Drake's objectives when he was planning to penetrate the Pacific in 1577. He did, indeed, on his circumnavigation of 1577–80 make a halfhearted attempt to sail westwards from the Strait of Magellan in search of the continent, but soon abandoned it for the pleasanter risks of preying on Spanish treasure-ships off the South American coast.

The old project of Sebastian Cabot, Robert Thorne and Roger Barlow for the discovery of a northerly passage to Asia was also revived. In

1565 Humphrey Gilbert began to interest himself in the scheme, and in the following year argued out with Anthony Jenkinson, a prominent agent of the Muscovy Company, before the Privy Council, the relative merits of expeditions to the north-west and north-east. The two joined forces to ask the Queen to authorize an expedition to the north-west, and Gilbert marshalled the theoretical evidence in *A Discourse of a Discoverie for a New Passage to Cataia*. After a brief interval in Ireland, Gilbert returned to urge the government to brush aside the opposition of the Muscovy Company to the grant of a patent for this purpose. He was unsuccessful. In 1574 Michael Lok, who had long been interested in a similar scheme, joined forces with Martin Frobisher, and they were successful in quashing the objections of the Muscovy Company. Gilbert's old pamphlet was published in 1576, by George Gascoigne, as propaganda for the enterprise. In the same year Frobisher discovered an inlet just north of the entrance to Hudson Bay, which he believed opened the sea-road to Asia, and he also brought home specimens of alleged gold-bearing ore. Officials, courtiers and merchants rushed to put money into the venture. Lok's Company of Cathay sent Frobisher to bring home 200 tons of ore in October 1577. Drake, on the point of departure, was told to search for the Pacific end of the passage. Though the ore did not yield more than

a few disputable traces of gold, belief lasted
long enough to enable Frobisher to make a third
expedition in 1578. Before his return with a
large cargo, confidence in the ore had vanished
and, amid a series of scandals and bankruptcies,
the Company of Cathay came to an end. It was
important as the first venture which received
public support for the exploitation of overseas
territory outside the range of Spanish authority.
Yet its double failure, and more especially the
gold fiasco, made investors suspicious of such
gold-finding projects. The derision which
greeted Sir Walter Raleigh's claims to have
located gold in Guiana in 1595 derived in part
from memory of this earlier failure.

The objectives of English overseas enterprise
thus far were threefold. First the extension of
commerce with Russia, North Africa, West
Africa and the eastern Mediterranean. Second,
piratical attacks on Spanish-American colonies,
mainly for loot. Third, searches for northerly
passages to Asia, which continued to provide an
incentive to a few intellectual speculators. The
establishment of English colonies of settlement
in temperate climates outside Europe was still, in
1578, a minor consideration. Yet, inside the
British Isles, Englishmen had for a generation
been making experiments in establishing
colonies. The field was Ireland. Henry VIII had
expended much effort in trying to establish
effective English authority over semi-inde-

pendent feudal lords and entirely independent Irish princes after 1534, and achieved only very limited success. The English authorities were specially concerned to extend the anglicized area of the Pale around Dublin, and to protect it against Irish attacks. Between 1548 and 1556 an attempt was being made to settle small groups of English farmer-soldiers round the garrisons in the Irish territories of Leix and Offaly. This developed, in the latter years of Mary's reign, into a more elaborate plantation, and was accompanied by schemes for a similar settlement in Ulster. Only a relatively small number of settlers were established in King's and Queen's Counties, where they were continually harassed by the Irish. Nevertheless, they formed the first English colony of the sixteenth century.

After 1565 the English government was almost continuously concerned with schemes for the extension of its authority in Ireland by means of further colonies. Because the establishment of English settlers by the state had proved so expensive, most of the projects of the next ten years were for settlements of groups of private speculators. It was in Ireland in the decade after 1565 that Englishmen became accustomed to the conception of a real colony of settlement, involving the transplantation of a section of English society overseas, where it must find a livelihood with the aid of cheap land and native labour. A large number of gentlemen, mainly from the south-western counties of England, many of whom served in the army in Ireland, were concerned in these projects. Ireland appeared to offer both plentiful land and profitable occupations for those ambitious younger sons, whose position was causing concern to officials and social thinkers.

Humphrey Gilbert, as a soldier in Ireland, had been attracted by Irish plantation schemes as early as 1566, and he was involved with Sir Arthur Champernoun in various plans for settlements in Ulster and Munster between 1566 and 1572. Sir Warham Saintleger and Richard Grenville had been doing propaganda in Devon and Cornwall for Irish colonies. Experiments were made in establishing privately financed colonies in Ulster between 1571 and 1575, the most interesting of them by Sir Thomas Smith, Elizabeth's Secretary of State. None achieved any lasting success. The Queen joined the Earl of Essex in a costly and unsuccessful attempt to settle County Antrim. In fact, few of these plans got beyond paper prospectuses. Their importance was that they familiarized a considerable number of Englishmen with the idea of colonizing lands outside their own country, not for the purpose of trading with wealthy Asiatic societies or working rich mines, but for the recreation of a mixed agricultural and commercial society like England. The desire to become a landed magnate with large numbers of tenants and towns inside his demesne took firm hold on Sir Humphrey Gilbert, as the result of his Irish experiences and projects. When he transferred his objective from Ireland to America, he initiated the first attempts, in which Walter Raleigh was actively concerned, to settle English colonies across the Atlantic.

Gilbert, who was some fifteen years older than his half-brother, had had a typical younger son's career. After Eton and Oxford, he had been attached to the household of the Princess Elizabeth, followed by brief residence in one of the Inns of Chancery. He had commanded a company of soldiers in the ill-fated English expedition to Le Havre in 1562–3, and on his return he pursued the north-west passage project between 1565 and 1568; but for most of the time between 1566 and 1570 he was employed as a soldier in Ireland, becoming interested in land settlement there and being knighted for his military services. In 1572 he commanded a force of 'volunteers' in the Netherlands, but returned to seek profitable government employment which was not forthcoming, though he married well and gained a fair income from his wife's lands. He took out his old 'Discourse' on the north-west passage, and polished it a little for George Gascoigne to publish in 1576. In 1577 he became interested in the projects for disrupting the Spanish-American empire. He thought of going to help John Oxenham, who had got cut off on the Panama Isthmus with captured treasure, but probably soon got news of his capture by the Spaniards. At the end of the year he put up schemes to the government for weakening Spanish maritime power by seizing her New-foundland fishing fleet, attacking the treasure fleet on its way to Europe and occupying the islands of Hispaniola and Cuba as permanent bases. In this he identified himself with the party at Court which desired to make a frontal challenge to Spanish imperial power, but he received no encouragement from the government, which still hoped to avoid committing England finally to war.

About this time Walter Raleigh, then some twenty-four years of age, became actively associated with his elder half-brother. They had both been residing in London, and overseas projects were common talk in the circle where they mixed; while George Gascoigne was at least one acquaintance they had in common outside their family group. Both had restless and intelligent minds, considerable ambitions and a lack of exciting or remunerative employment. Walter Raleigh was clearly very much the junior partner in the scheme.

After 1577 Gilbert concentrated all his energies and resources on his plans to establish English colonies in North America. He transmitted his enthusiasm to his half-brother, and between them they developed those experiments which, in spite of their failure, were an essential background to the successful ventures of the seventeenth century. Some English geographers were also thinking of North America as a suitable field for English settlement. Richard Hakluyt, the elder, a lawyer and a consultant on overseas geography and trade, had been collecting information for some years, and was to help Gilbert with advice on American colonization in 1578. His younger cousin, the Rev. Richard Hakluyt, was also involved. In 1578 Gilbert was specially interested in Norumbega, the name given to the North American coastline roughly between the Hudson River and Cape Breton, and in Newfoundland. The latter had some attractions as a site for a settlement, because of the possiblity of controlling profitably the big international fishery off its shores.

Gilbert's patent of June 11, 1578, authorized him to search for and occupy with English settlers lands 'not actually possessed of any Christian prince or people.' He was given six years in which to acquire lands overseas, and was to hold title to them from the Crown. He was already collecting ships, and apparently hoped to leave during the summer. His principal co-adventurer was Henry Knollys, son of Sir Francis Knollys, treasurer of the household. Gilbert relied largely, however, on his own family. He realized some of his wife's property, and got subscriptions from his brothers, Sir John and Adrian Gilbert. As active participants, he brought in both Walter Raleigh and his elder brother Carew. Thus five of Katherine Champernoun's sons were involved in the venture, as well as several Champernoun and Carew cousins.

During the delays which occurred in equipping the fleet of ten ships at Plymouth, quarrels broke out between Knollys and Gilbert which ended in the former sailing off with three of the vessels to desert colonial pioneering for piracy in the Channel and the Bay of Biscay. Only on November 19 could Gilbert finally set out, with seven ships. One was commanded by him, one by Carew Raleigh and one by Walter Raleigh. The latter was the *Falcon*, an old ship of 100 tons, owned by William Hawkins, John's brother, the fourth largest in the fleet. As captain, Raleigh was not expected to be an expert seaman, and his duty was to maintain discipline and command the men in action. The navigator, who would manage the ship, was the master, Simon Fernandez, a Portuguese pilot who was to play a prominent part in later enterprises. Half a dozen gentlemen sailed with them, and the total complement of seventy included a number of soldiers.

As the Spanish ambassador and his agents showed a good deal of interest, the precise objective of the expedition was kept secret. All the more reliable indications are that it was intended to cross the Atlantic by way of the Canaries to the West Indies, and to work up the North American coast in the following spring. The heavy armament carried was needed to repel any Spanish vessels encountered on the voyage. The expedition was not intended to do more than explore part of the coast, in preparation for a colonizing expedition after a suitable site had been found.

The *Falcon* was so leaky and ill-supplied that Gilbert had to take his squadron into an Irish port for repairs. When he set out again he encountered such bad weather that his vessels were scattered and he, himself, had to return to England. The *Red Lion* slipped off to join Knollys and was later lost at sea. The *Falcon*, under Fernandez's direction, hoped to make for a part of the North American coast which the pilot knew. She turned southwards and picked up some food supplies at Grand Canary. She then made for the West Indies 'to do something worthy honour' and on her way, perhaps as far south as the Cape Verdes, had a brush with Spanish or Portuguese ships. She escaped with some damage. How near she got to the West Indies is not known, but she had to return and limped back to England in May 1579.

Back in England, both Gilbert and Raleigh wished to renew their voyage in the summer of 1579. But the piracy committed by Knollys had caused trouble, and Gilbert's men had made away with a Spanish vessel, so it is not surprising

that the Privy Council issued orders to prevent
them setting out to sea. Legal inquiries required
their presence in England, and the government,
however tolerant of plundering that took place
in American waters, did not at this time tolerate
indiscriminate piracy nearer home. Nothing that
is known incriminates Gilbert or Raleigh per-
sonally in the seizure of French and Spanish
ships. The government found an alternative use
for such of the vessels as were still seaworthy by
ordering them to intercept James Fitzmaurice,
a rebellious Munster nobleman, who was on his
way to Ireland to challenge English authority
there. Gilbert, possibly accompanied by Raleigh,
missed Fitzmaurice, who landed safely in Ireland. Gilbert was then employed on government
service on the Irish coast, though Raleigh did
not remain with him. By the end of 1579 the
first colonizing project appeared to have fizzled
out.

Between 1579 and 1583 there was a great
change in Raleigh's fortunes. When he had set
sail with Gilbert he was still one of a swarm of
young men who hung about the Court, striving
to make a brave show on little and looking out
for employment or for opportunities to make
money by private speculation. By 1583, when
Raleigh was again to participate in a colonizing
expedition led by his half-brother, he occupied
quite a different position. He had caught and
held the attention of the Queen, and appeared

31

to be making his way to prominence at Court.

While Gilbert had gone on Irish service Raleigh had proceeded to Court, and had rapidly won, if not yet favour, at least notoriety. He is found on terms of intimacy with prominent courtiers and carried a challenge from the Earl of Oxford, Burghley's son-in-law, to the young Sir Philip Sidney. His hot temper and pride brought about a quarrel with Sir Thomas Perrot, which in turn led to both parties spending a short time in prison in February 1580, while within a few weeks after his release he was sent to gaol again for an affray beside the tennis-court at Westminster. Besides gaining the reputation of an unruly gallant, he had made himself known to three of the men who counted most in the government—Leicester, Burghley and Walsingham. The last, at least, appears to have been impressed by his keen analytical mind and restless energy. In the summer of 1580 he got what he needed most, employment and a chance to prove his practical capacity. He was sent as captain of a company of soldiers to Ireland.

In Ireland there was fighting in plenty to be done. Fitzmaurice had landed with a commission from the Pope to liberate the island from the excommunicated Queen Elizabeth. English power there was at a low ebb. Attempts to settle colonists had failed and no effective brake had been placed on the unruly Anglo-Irish magnates in Munster. Fitzmaurice found plenty of inflammable material on which to work. He mobilized almost all the Anglo-Irish of Munster in a struggle, ostensibly, for religious liberty, but really for feudal licence against the centralizing English power, and he also got support from autonomous Irish rulers unwilling to tolerate the surrender of their native social order for one designed on English models.

Fitzmaurice's continental mercenaries entrenched themselves at Smerwick in Kerry, but neither insurgents nor English acted decisively, taking long to assemble their strength and making the war a protracted and devastating one. When the threat to English power in Ireland was at last appreciated, the cumbrous military machine was got in motion under Lord Grey of Wilton, who, by the time Raleigh arrived in Ireland, was getting ready to wipe out the Smerwick garrison. Raleigh's men were quickly employed in the siege and assault. On November 10 the garrison surrendered. Grey thereupon sent in two companies, one of which was Raleigh's, to kill everyone, mercenaries and Irish, men and women, except for a handful of prisoners. Controversy has raged from that day to this on whether Grey accepted the surrender on terms and then broke them. If the garrison yielded unconditionally, such laws of war as there were condoned the killings. It is not certain that Raleigh took a personal part in the massacre, but if he did it was as a soldier under orders, although there is no reason to suppose he would have objected to his gruesome task. The killings were intended to make clear to the continental powers that any invasion of English territory would be met with the utmost ruthlessness. The Smerwick landing, sponsored by the Pope and connived at by Philip, was the second round in a struggle of which the northern rising of 1569 had been the first.

During the year and a half that Raleigh remained in Ireland, he was treated by both Grey and the English government as something more than an ordinary company commander. In August 1580 he had been put on a judicial commission to try the Earl of Desmond's brother. His men were employed to occupy the strongholds of Anglo-Irish nobles suspected of sympathy with the insurgents. He showed courage, vigour and a harsh competence in minor military actions.

Early in 1581, writing to Walsingham, he criticized Ormond, now military commander in Munster, who was unwilling to engage in an all-out offensive which would alienate the Munster gentry from his own family. Raleigh regarded the rising as an intolerable affront to royal authority. He urged Walsingham to send over Sir Humphrey Gilbert to terrorize the insurgents into final submission. Later he urged Grey to send more troops to hunt down the rebels. When Ormond relinquished his command, Raleigh was appointed one of three commissioners to govern Munster for the time being. He soon tired of the Irish service, however, and wrote to Leicester in August: 'I have spent some time here under the deputy, in such place and charge as, were it not for that I knew him to be one of yours, I would disdain it as much as to keep sheep.' The note of arrogance, self-assurance and ambition is evident.

When he returned in December 1581 with despatches, he had no intention of going back to Ireland. In England Raleigh offered Burghley advice on Munster and criticized Grey for inefficiency. Burghley was still consulting him at the end of 1582, and it was his Irish service which gave Raleigh his first taste of responsibility.

In the month or two after his arrival from Ireland, Raleigh attracted the Queen's attention. Elizabeth would, on her Sunday ceremonial processions, pick out some gentleman or other whom she did not know. If he looked and spoke well and continued to please, this might be a first step into the small circle of her intimate friends, whom she treated informally and with whom she conducted bantering and familiar conversations and correspondence, tinged with the unreal though useful conventions of courtly love and chivalry.

Raleigh was soon spoken of as a new favourite, and he evidently made a very strong impression on the Queen. Yet to become her friend did not necessarily bring profits or employment. A new recruit to her circle had to prove that he had something more than a good appearance and manner before he was entrusted with any responsibility. In the spring of 1582, the Queen was thinking of Raleigh as one who would make a valuable servant when he had more experience. She therefore proposed to send him back to Ireland to be 'trained some time longer in that our realm for his better experience in martial affairs.' Somehow he avoided going, and by the autumn had made rapid progress with the Queen, receiving as a sign of his admission to her circle of intimates the nickname 'Water'— a play on his Christian name.

He was not likely to be content with a purely decorative position, but aimed at power as well. In a letter to Walsingham in 1582, he had urged that Sir Humphrey Gilbert be given better employment by the Queen, and added 'would God his own behaviour were such in peace as it did not make his good service forgotten and hold him from the preferment he is worthy of.' This throws some light on Raleigh himself. Gilbert's temper and his capacity for grousing made him a bad courtier, and he had never received any important favour from the Queen, whom he had served since he was a boy. Raleigh implied that he was not going to spoil his own chances by giving rein to his temper or by scorning the graces of Court life. Equally he was determined to gain preferment fitting to his own high opinion of his capacities. First employed on a number of small tasks at Court and in administration, soon substantial rewards began to come to him.

The spring and summer of Raleigh's career lasted from May 1583 to July 1592. He became increasingly prominent at Court as the Queen's close friend, and Elizabeth entrusted him with considerable administrative authority, even if she did not allow him much influence in the making of high policy, and was increasingly troubled by his resentment at new admissions to the intimate circle of her friends. She paid him well; and the impoverished gentleman became the wealthy and magnificent courtier.[1] The grant, in May 1583, of a monopoly of issuing licences for the sale of wine provided a basic income. He farmed his rights for £700–£800 a year at first, and later received some £1,300 from this source. From March 1584 onwards he also obtained a series of profitable licences to export cloth freed from statutory restrictions. Later, at the height of his prosperity, came a pension of £2,000 a year from the customs. Licences and monopolies were Eliza-

[1] One of the best acounts of these years is in E. G. Clark, *Ralegh and Marlowe* (1941).

beth's favourite means of rewarding her favourites but they were detested by merchants, manufacturers and consumers alike, and brought their recipients unpopularity, especially, as in Raleigh's case, when they were exploited harshly and rapaciously. As Member of Parliament for Devonshire from 1584, Raleigh was expected to defend royal prerogatives against attack, though he did not do so consistently. He was knighted and, in 1585, given his first administrative office, that of Lord Warden of the Stannaries. This made him not only responsible for the Cornish tin-mines but also law-maker and judge in the mining areas. The grant of the lord-lieutenancy of Cornwall and of the vice-admiralty of Devon and Cornwall, which followed, completed the delegation to him of most of the royal authority over the south-western counties and, until 1603, he occupied a position of outstanding influence there. His half-brother, Sir John Gilbert, became his deputy in the Devonshire vice-admiralty, and together they could mobilize the shipping of the south-western ports and make money out of the activity of privateers and pirates. Though always avaricious, Raleigh did not regard his offices solely as a means of making money, and proved an able and conscientious administrator. But his interests continued to be centred in the Court, and in 1587 he became captain of the guard and so responsible for the Queen's personal safety;

while, to enable him to cut a still better figure, he received from Elizabeth lands confiscated from the Babington plotters.

In all this rush of advancement Raleigh did not forget, was indeed never to forget, those overseas ambitions which had been stirred in him by the fruitless voyage of 1578. While he was becoming a favourite, an administrator, a rich man, he not only kept his colonial objectives in mind but also did a great deal to foster their realization. Only now, and until his disgrace in 1592, he was to be an agent rather than an instrument. His task was to support, to inspire and to organize enterprises overseas, but not to take part in them himself. In these years he was too close to the Queen for her to let him go far away, and certainly not on risky voyages into the almost unknown.

His first task as he rose at Court was to assist Sir Humphrey Gilbert in preparing his last elaborate and unfortunate venture. Gilbert had not stopped grumbling about the money the government owed him for his services in Irish waters before he was again planning the American colonies, which were now the focus for all his ambitions. Early in 1580 he had sent out his little frigate, the *Squirrel*, of only eight tons burden, under Simon Fernandez, to make a reconnaissance on the other side of the Atlantic. In three months Fernandez had coasted the American shore, probably making a landing in

New England, and bringing back information about the land and its Indian inhabitants. Equipped with this instalment of first-hand knowledge of North America, Gilbert set about realizing his own depleted properties and enlisting all and sundry as subscribers to his enterprice. Renouncing his claims north of 50° to that learned devotee of the north-west passage, the astrologer John Dee, he built up in 1582-3 a vast paper scheme for the distribution and exploitation of the new lands.

He placed his main emphasis on land to arouse the cupidity of the land-hungry young men of his own social group. He held out the prospect that for a small investment gentlemen might find themselves suddenly transformed into feudal lords of great estates on which towns and tenancies might be multiplied quickly and cheaply. There was novelty and force about this appeal to investors and adventurers. At the same time, many of Gilbert's hearers were more sceptical than he of the possibilities of rapid developments in colonization. They were also on their guard against such another will-o'-the-wisp as the Company of Cathay. As economic incentives, Gilbert thought gold and jewels might be mentioned (thought without too great emphasis); also raw materials which could be produced and acquired more cheaply than those bought from foreign countries; and finally, possibilities of export markets for manufactures, first among

40

the Indians and later among the settlers. These were objectives which would appeal to the business-like investor, and more especially to merchants, without whose help and capital the colony would have difficulty in maintaining itself. Then, too, America might be advertised as a place of refuge for those who could not fit into the tightening ecclesiastical system of the Elizabethan state, and, in particular, the loyal Catholic gentry who had not been seduced by the papal excommunication or by Philip II to transfer their allegiance from Elizabeth.

Between June 1582 and February 1583 Gilbert disposed of nearly 9,000,000 acres of land, on paper, to intending colonists of New England, mostly to Catholic gentlemen, who undertook to exploit their grants under his supreme command. They intended, in the first place, to send out on their own account a reconnaissance expedition in 1582, to be followed early in 1583 by a large colonizing expedition under three well-known commanders, Sir William Stanley, Richard Bingham and Martin Frobisher. Gilbert planned that he, with what money he could get from his friends and relations, should make a further reconnaissance in 1582, and a more substantial expedition in the following year to establish a settlement parallel with the Catholic venture. An agreement with the merchants of Southampton at the end of 1582 promised them a monopoly of trade with the colonies in return for financial assistance.

Attempts were made to collect information about North America. The younger Richard Hakluyt, who had become a stout supporter of Gilbert's project, helped in this work by the publication of his *Divers Voyages Touching the Discoverie of America* (the forerunner of the famous *Principal Navigations*), which was intended to stimulate public interest in North America, and specifically in Gilbert's venture. In August and September 1582 Sir Francis Walsingham presided over an inquiry into the information provided by David Ingram (who claimed to have walked from the Gulf of Mexico to the vicinity of Cape Breton), Simon Fernandez and others.

Most of the Catholic gentlemen, apart from Sir George Peckham, were warned off by their priests and by the propaganda of the Spanish ambassador. They were told that if they went they would be deserters in the struggle for the faith in England, and if they ever arrived they would have their throats cut by the Spaniards. The result was that neither of their projected expeditions came to anything. Christopher Carleill, Walsingham's stepson, on the pretext of mobilizing the Bristol merchants behind Gilbert, attempted to double-cross him and to launch an independent project with the backing of the Bristol merchants and the wealthy Muscovy Company.

Gilbert found money hard to come by, and this held up his venture month by month, while his sailors ate into the provisions and stores. In February 1583 a new obstacle presented itself. The Queen suggested that he should not accompany the expedition in person, as he was 'a man noted of not good hap at sea;' but she did not prohibit his departure and he determined to proceed with his plans. Elizabeth had shown her liking for Gilbert by her intervention and took his refusal in good part. She got Walter Raleigh to write to him on March 16 to say 'she wished great good hap and safety to your ships as if herself were there in person,' and to convey to him a token of her esteem—'an anchor guided by a lady.'

It is probable that Raleigh wished to go himself, but his position at Court was such that the Queen was unlikely to part with him. He was certainly deeply interested in the preparations, and contributed its largest ship to the expedition, the *Bark Raleigh*, of 200 tons, commanded by Michael Butler, who had been lieutenant of Raleigh's old company in Ireland, and with a Bristol man, Robert Davis, as master. Raleigh's investment was estimated at £2,000, a very substantial sum for him to raise at a time when royal favour was just beginning to bring him monetary rewards. At the rate Gilbert was offering, this would entitle him to an estate of 400,000 acres in America.

The expedition sailed on June 11 for New-foundland, intending to make its way down the American coast, but on June 13 the *Bark Raleigh* turned back home and put in at Plymouth. Gilbert was furious at this desertion. He wrote back from Newfoundland to Sir George Peckham, 'I pray you solicit my brother Rawley to make them an example of all knaves.' Edward Hayes, who wrote the narrative of Gilbert's voyage, said they had put back because of an outbreak of infectious disease. But one of the sailors, questioned in the Admiralty Court some weeks later, said simply that Butler had returned 'for want of victuals to perform the voyage.' It is only too probable that this was the correct reason, as delays, and possibly embezzlement by the crew, may well have depleted the stores below the limit of safety. The result was that Raleigh, after all, had no share in his half-brother's fatal voyage.

While Gilbert's objective was Norumbega and his chief interest at his departure was in the southern part of the later New England, he determined to secure control of Newfoundland, as his patent entitled him to do. For many years Portuguese, Spanish, French and English fisher-men had each summer allocated drying stages on land for the cod they caught. They also had a system of arbitration for the settlement of disputes between them. Gilbert believed that it would be a blow to Spain, by eliminating the

Spanish fishing-boats, if he put the island under English jurisdiction, while he might make money by leasing sites on shore to the fishermen. Consequently, on August 5, 1583, he assembled the fishermen at the harbour of St. John's, and formally annexed the island to the English Crown, demanding also the payment of rents to him for the use of drying stages. He spent a fortnight prospecting for minerals and exploring the country, and he apparently came to believe it would be possible to establish a colony there. He had to send one ship home with sick men and did not leave any permanent garrison on the island. With the *Delight*, the *Golden Hind* and the tiny *Squirrel*, he set out on August 10 for America. Eight days later the *Delight* went aground and was wrecked, either on Sable Island or near Cape Breton. His sailors became discontented after this disaster and, as food was short, Gilbert turned back on August 31, without having achieved any important part of his objectives. On the return voyage, in spite of heavy seas, Gilbert insisted on remaining in the *Squirrel*. On September 9 she disappeared without trace. Edward Hayes, in the *Golden Hind*, brought home the sad news to Sir George Peckham and Raleigh. The first considerable project for English colonization of North America was at an end. The onus of continuing Gilbert's work was thrown on Sir George Peckham, Christopher Carleill and Walter Raleigh. It was

Raleigh who was to make the greatest efforts and to come nearest to success. To encourage him he had at least salved his ship from the wreckage of Gilbert's hopes and fortune.[1]

[1] For the details of Gilbert's expeditions, see D. B. Quinn, *The Voyages and Colonising Expeditions of Sir Humphrey Gilbert*, 2 vols. (1940).

Chapter Three

The English Approach to America

THE English approach to America had been for nearly a century a very slow and tentative one; now at last it was becoming definite. With the colonizing expeditions which Raleigh sent out, Englishmen came to grips with the realities of the American continent.

From Cabot's earliest discoveries onwards interest had centred on the possibility of rounding the American land-mass, or of penetrating it by a passage in temperate latitudes, as a way to reach the riches of farther Asia. These preoccupations on the part of a long line of men—Sebastian Cabot, Robert Thorne, Michael Lok, Humphrey Gilbert (for a time), Martin Frobisher, John Dee, Adrian Gilbert and John Davis among them—had obscured interest in the mainland, its peoples, its products and its possiblities, which it was necessary to arouse before men went to explore and settle there.

The discovery of the Newfoundland Banks by John Cabot created the first firm links between England and the new western lands. Hundreds of English fishermen learnt something of ocean seafaring on the Atlantic, and of the small stretches of coast on which they established their stages for drying fish. But before Gilbert's intervention, few of them had turned their eyes from the immediate task of fishing to observe the land about them or speculate about its exploitation. Few, if any, Englishmen contributed to the cartography which eventually revealed the outlines of the American lands— first of Newfoundland, and then of other parts of the coastline. This was the work of Portuguese and Frenchmen, and Italians in their employment. Hakluyt and Raleigh in the 'eighties were still relying on maps and descriptions of Giovanni da Verrazano, who explored New England sixty years before, and on the records of Cartier's and Roberval's voyages to Canada between 1534 and 1543.

Florida, as the Spaniards called the coastline as far north as modern Virginia, was better known in England. French Huguenots settled there in 1562, and one of their leaders, Jean Ribault, came to England to ask for help. In 1563 Thomas Stukely organized an expedition, in aid of which Ribault published an account of his experiences in Florida; but the ships never reached America. Piracy in home waters proved too attractive. A second French colony, under René Laudonnière, was visited by Hawkins in 1565, shortly before it was destroyed by a Spanish expedition. Narratives of these expeditions were studied by Hakluyt for evidence on

North American conditions, and in 1586 he had one of them published in Paris, with a dedication to Raleigh. More important, Jacques le Moyne de Morgues, painter and cartographer with Laudonnière, settled in England after 1572. and his maps, paintings of American-Indian life and narratives were placed at Raleigh's disposal. It was this material on Florida which first gave Raleigh and his friends a vivid and realistic impression of North American conditions. Yet, even so, they embarked on plans for establishing colonies with very little accurate information of the mainland, and with particularly slight knowledge of the coastline where they intended to plant settlements.

From 1565 onwards, Spaniards had tried to establish themselves on the Atlantic seaboard. They made elaborate attempts to settle farmers and traders, as well as a garrison, in Florida. A French raid in 1568 was not followed up. Yet the colony did not flourish. Only St. Augustine became a sizable town; while an outpost was maintained at Santa Elena, far to the north in modern South Carolina.[1] The Spaniards wished to deny the coast to settlement by other European powers; they also wished to guard against the establishment of a base from which the treasure fleets, sailing through the Florida Channel, north-eastward bound for Spain, might be intercepted and attacked. It was to the area

[1] Parris Island, Port Royal Sound, near Beaufort.

immediately north of the loosely held Spanish zone that Raleigh decided to direct his colonists.

He did not make this decision immediately after news came of Gilbert's disappearance. His first thought was to join with Adrian Gilbert and John Davis, a Dartmouth sea-captain, in exploiting Gilbert's discarded exploration rights in the region north of Newfoundland, but by February 1584 he had given up the idea of attempting to find a north-west passage. Adrian Gilbert received a patent to do so, and under his authority John Davis made a series of brilliant exploring voyages between 1585 and 1587. On his third voyage he penetrated far into Baffin Bay in 73° north latitude, but he achieved no economic returns and did not find a workable passage to Asia. Raleigh remained in touch with this venture, and may have invested some money in it, for in 1588 he was associated in an abortive attempt to reorganize the company of adventurers and to prepare further expeditions.

In the latter months of 1583 and the beginning of 1584, Sir George Peckham, Christopher Carleill and others were preparing expeditions to establish colonies in North America, but failed to put any ships to sea before Raleigh applied for, and was granted, on March 25, 1584, a new patent transferring to him Gilbert's rights under his patent of 1578, but excepting the power to exercise any monopoly over the Newfoundland fishery. This gave him exclusive rights to control access to territory within 600 miles to the north and south of any settlement he should establish within six years.

By this time he had made up his mind in what part of America he wished to plant his English colony. Adrian Gilbert's vision was set on those northern shores which might lead him to China; Sir John Gilbert may have been planning to exploit Sir Humphrey's annexation of Newfoundland; Peckham's objective was New England. Raleigh turned his attention to the zone of Mediterranean climate farther south, which lay to the north of the Spanish outposts in Florida.

He did not intend to approach the American coastline by the difficult voyage south from Newfoundland or by the untried route directly across the Atlantic, but preferred the known track of the English pirates to the Spanish West Indies, by the Canaries, along which it was possible to get fresh water and provisions, and from which wind and current would take his ships northwards past Spanish Florida.

By the time the patent was sealed his preparations were already advanced, for on April 27, only a month later, two small ships set out from a south-western port for an American reconnaissance. They were under the command of Philip Amadas, a Plymouth man, and Arthur Barlow, with Simon Fernandez, who had made the daring voyage for Gilbert in 1580, as pilot. The ships reached the West Indies by June 10 and, after taking on water and provisions, sailed up the mainland coast at the beginning of July. Their first landing was made on Hatteras, a low sandy island forming part of the Carolina Outer Banks. Of this they took possession in the name of the Queen.

The appearance and atmosphere of American landscape is brought to life for us in Arthur Barlow's brief description:

'We viewed the land about us, being, whereas we first landed, very sandy and low towards the water's side, but so full of grapes as the very beating and surge of the sea overflowed them of which we found such plenty, as well there as in all places else, both on the sand and on the green soil on the hills, as in the plains, as well on every little shrub, as also climbing towards the tops of high cedars, that I think in all the world the like abundance is not to be found.

'We passed from the sea side towards the tops of those hills next adjoining, being but of mean height, and from thence we beheld the sea on both sides. Under the bank or hill whereon we stood, we beheld the valleys replenished with goodly cedar trees, and having discharged our harquebus-shot, such a flock of cranes (the most part white) arose under us, with such a cry redoubled by many echoes, as if an army of men had shouted all together.'

The third day brought the first contact with the natives. A canoe, with three Indians, came along the shore. One of them landed and went ahead to look at the ships riding at anchor. A boat was sent, and he came willingly, trying to make himself understood by signs. He was given food and drink, a hat, shirt and other presents, and taken back. He immediately joined his companions in fishing and soon gave his return present, a canoe-load of fish carefully divided between the two ships.

In such simplicity the explorers began their mission, in clear summer days, by a sandy reef covered with grass, amid abundant vegetation and tall impressive trees, with fish and fowl abounding, and the Indians mild, curious and friendly.

The first meeting was a prelude to more extensive bargaining. Visited by Granganimeo, the brother of the tribal chieftain of Roanoke Island, they gathered that the Indian name for the whole region was Wingandacoa, and that the tribal centre was some six days' journey by canoe. Pots and pans, tools and weapons, were briskly exchanged for dressed and undressed skins and furs. Pearls were offered for armour. Meat, fruit and vegetables were brought as gifts. Barlow had a special word to say for maize —'their country corn, which is very white, fair and well tasted'—and marvelled at the ease with which it could be grown.

A little later a party made its way to Roanoke,

an island lying between the reef and the shore, near the opening of Albemarle Sound. There they saw the tiny tribal village 'of nine houses, built of cedar, and fortified round about with sharp trees, to keep out their enemies, and the entrance into it made like a turn-pike very artificially.' They were hospitably entertained, and Barlow had nothing but praise for his hosts —'a more kind and loving people there can not be found in the world, as far as we have hitherto had trial.' They were willing to pass on information—precisely how it was conveyed we cannot tell—about the mainland and its inhabitants, which Barlow noted. No more was thought necessary.

The vessels reached England again in September, with two Indians, Manteo and Wanchese, from Roanoke, and their samples of Indian wares. They reported a rich and hospitable land, ready for settlement and sparsely peopled by Indians who were simple, virile and friendly— a transatlantic paradise only awaiting its English settlers. This was all that Raleigh could ask, but it was not all that he needed to know before he sent out colonists.

The explorers had failed to find a good harbour. They had brought their small barks, 'though not without some difficulty,' into the first haven they found. They had been fortunate in the weather and could not know of the gales, the sharp thunderstorms and violent hurricanes which swept the coast. On all the long reef there was no harbour which could shelter a ship of even 100 tons. For that they must have gone another 100 miles north of Roanoke to the Chesapeake. This was to prejudice the establishment of a settlement and to rob it of all strategic significance. Pamlico Sound, behind the reef, was very shallow, and the one major deep-water inlet, Albemarle Sound, could not be entered through the reef by anything more than twenty-ton pinnaces.

There was reason for optimism in the good reports of the climate and the vegetation. Temperature, rainfall and length of the growing season were almost all that could be desired. There was a great variety of trees and plants useful to man. Fish and game were plentiful. But there were disadvantages. The great fertility of some of the soil obscured the fact that much of it was unfit for cultivation. Many of the more open fertile sites were the seat of Indian villages. To avoid disrupting them meant clearing the forest or going up the estuaries where the colonists would be largely cut off from contact with such harbours as there were. Pioneering here might not be so hard as it was later for the first New Englanders, but it was not too easy. The illusion of a fat land awaiting to pour its riches into English laps was one of the misleading impressions which Barlow's picture was bound to create.

Barlow's is the first English report on the North American Indians, but from his sketch and the later records of the English explorers, we can get a fair picture of the coastal peoples with whom they came into contact. They were agriculturists, yet not too firmly fixed in their settlements. Their garden crops, mainly grown by women, were tended carefully. The main crop was maize, of which successive sowings were made in the spring and summer. But beans, many types of gourd, and, with special attention, tobacco were also grown. The ground was very fertile and was not manured, but when it had become useless a new patch was cleared from the forest. The Indians were expert fishermen, building long fish-weirs of flexible reeds out into the sounds, and using dug-out canoes. Roots, fruit, shell-fish and turtle helped to supplement their crops, and they hunted deer and bear. They had no domestic animals, except dogs.

The coastal villages were small, containing simple houses of bark or reed mats over a pole framework for from nine to thirty families. The chief's house and the temple, where the desiccated ancestors of the chief and the tribal gods were housed, were larger and more substantial. Circles of carved posts formed another focus for their animistic religion. Some villages, like Secoton, were open; others, like Pomeioc, were closely palisaded. In them pottery was made, but no cloth, Reeds were plaited into mats, deer-skins finely dressed and ornamented. Copper and a little silver were used for decoration and exchange, but all tools and weapons were of wood, bone and stone. The war tomahawk was another form of the stone axe they used for shaping timber.

Their tribal units were small, sometimes including only a single village, sometimes as many as thirty. Wars about hunting and fishing grounds and robberies of crops were frequent. There was a little trade, with copper as a medium of exchange, between the tribes.

Barlow saw mainly their simplicity and their friendliness. This seemed to him a basis on which English colonists could build, but it was scarcely sufficient. The Indians certainly respected the white men, credited them with power to work miracles and believed them to be reincarnations from another world. However, a few weeks' contact with a small reconnaissance party was one thing and life with an active and permanent white settlement another.

The colonists of 1585–6 made heavy demands on the villages, asking for more of the small store of winter and seed corn than they could or would spare, constantly requiring them to construct fish-weirs and to supply food of all sorts. Anxious as they were to acquire copper, tools and metal objects of all kinds, their response was limited by an unwillingness to disturb their accustomed routine and become in effect the white men's servants. The latter behaved with some harshness on occasion, which bred resentment. This in turn aroused the cupidity of the Indians. As white men became more familiar, awe of them diminished and large-scale conflicts developed. Yet enmity was not continuous or universal, though for a small pioneer colony Indian relations were a constant problem and often a serious threat to survival. The larger issue lay behind. Could primitive peoples, living in sparsely populated areas and deriving much of their well-being from the extent of their hunting, fishing and garden grounds, exist side by side with a more complex, acquisitive, white community, with its ultimate demand for the bulk of the land? The future was to show that in most cases they could not. Indians never made good slaves, and it was not possible to adapt them easily to intensive and peaceful agriculture and commerce. The fate of the majority, after generations of strife, was extinction.

The reconnaissance made by Amadas and Barlow must have strained Raleigh's finances. He had saved his ship and some equipment out of the wreck of Gilbert's fortunes in 1583, but he was only beginning to make a sizable income from his offices and perquisites. His chief asset in obtaining financial assistance was his position at Court, where he could canvass his projects among wealthier men. Walsingham was his constant supporter, and was probably a considerable investor in the first voyage. Much more money must be found, however, if a colony was to be put on shore and supplied for a sojourn in America. That problem brought the younger Richard Hakluyt back from his embassy chaplaincy in Paris to consult with Raleigh in July 1584.

The result of their discussions was that Hakluyt wrote an exhaustive treatise on the prospects of English colonization for the Queen's information. Raleigh was convinced that these prospects were so attractive that the state should take on responsibility for establishing English rule in North America, as the rulers of Castile and Aragon had done for the Spanish Indies nearly a century before.

Hakluyt's treatise, which we know as the *Discourse of Western Planting*, was finished before Amadas and Barlow returned. He set himself to show that, on the basis of Cabot's discoveries, England had a prior claim to North America, and should, therefore, assume the government and the duty of civilizing and Christianizing its inhabitants. His major political argument was the blow this would inflict on Spain. Not only would English America soon outstrip Spanish America in power, but it would provide bases for striking alike at the treasure fleets from the West Indies and at the fishing fleets off Newfoundland. Spanish America, he argued, was much weaker than was supposed, and Spanish cruelties had made the native peoples a source of disruption. The Spanish empire could be overturned, and Europe freed from Spanish and Catholic domination.

The picture of a political revolution was balanced by an elaborate economic analysis. In North America the English would find all those products which they had to import from other European countries, or which they had to obtain at second or third hand from the Spanish and Portuguese empires; they would gain much commerce and great new profits whether or not gold and silver were also found. Further, England would find new markets for her own manufactures, alike among the to-be-civilized Indians and her own settlers. Sending colonists overseas would end unemployment in England, and the resultant commerce would prevent recurring economic distress. Hakluyt, in fact, promised an economic revolution as far-reaching as the political one.

This glowing argument was buttressed by a mass of detail, partly cogent and telling, partly academic or fantastic. Two elements stand out. The first was that the intended colony must provide a suitable base for maritime action against the treasure fleets and the West Indian islands; that was the short-term strategic objective. The second was to build up an economy on the other side of the Atlantic which would supply all kinds of Mediterranean fruits and their products, wine and oil, foodstuffs, dyes and drugs, and also, if possible, timber and ships' stores. Transatlantic sources for these commodities would render English trade independent of European countries, with their political difficulties, tariffs and taxes. This objective required a colony as far south on the Atlantic coast as was possible without exposing the colonists to constant attacks from Spanish Florida.

These objectives explain the reconnaissance expedition's route. Its failure to find a good harbour impoverished the prospects of the pioneering settlement, but this had still to be learnt by experience.

Hakluyt lists the types of emigrant that were needed—carpenters, millwrights and joiners to exploit timber resources; gardeners with a knowledge of vine and olive growing; craftsmen in dyes and minerals; builders; soldiers for defence. Men who had lost their money and self-respect, imprisoned debtors, ex-soldiers, children of wandering beggars; 'valiant youths rusting and hurtful by lack of employment'; Puritan clergy, who might convert the Indians instead of making trouble at home—all these could be spared as colonists. But he does not say how they should be organized, whether as members of a semi-military expedition, as servants of a commercial corporation, or as communities building a new society on their own farms.

This ambitious scheme suited Raleigh's roving mind and wide imagination, but it expected too much too soon. Hakluyt presented it to the Queen in October, and was well received and rewarded. Raleigh, doubtless, followed it up with the reports from America which Barlow brought to him. Elizabeth, however, was used to 'projects.' Her subjects were always asking her sanction for fine schemes to enrich themselves as well as her. She was not likely to take Raleigh's views, any more than Hakluyt's uncritically. Encouragement, and some investment in the expeditions, were all she was likely to give.

The first act of Amadas and Barlow on landing on the islands had been to take formal possession for Raleigh on behalf of the Crown. If he could confirm this by an actual settlement he could, under his patent, claim control over the future appropriation of the coastline between Spanish Florida and the coast of Maine. It was, therefore, important for him to get his title put on the soundest possible legal footing.

Raleigh had a bill introduced in the House of Commons to confirm his title to 'Wyngandacoia.' The name was, he tell us, given under a misapprehension: 'for when some of my people asked the name of that country, one of the savages answered, "Wingandacon," which is as much to say, as "You wear good clothes" or "Gay clothes." ' The bill passed through three readings between December 13 and 18, but limits were set to his power to obtain settlers and equipment for his colony. Imprisoned debtors, wives, wards and apprentices could not be taken; shipping and supplies must not be requisitioned. Though it got its first reading in the House of Lords on December 19 it was not proceeded with when the House reassembled in February after the Christmas recess. This was the first occasion on which American affairs came before an English parliament. Raleigh, however, was content with assurances from the Queen. She agreed the new land might be renamed Virginia in her honour—a name by which the greater part of the Atlantic coast was to be known in England for over thirty years. In return she knighted Walter Raleigh on January 6, 1585. He then had a seal made of his arms with an inscription describing him as 'Lord and Governor of Virginia.'

What material help the Queen gave is more difficult to discover. The customary method of organizing overseas expeditions for commerce or piracy was to raise subscriptions as a joint stock to be repaid with profit or loss at the end of the voyage. Since the costs of equipping and supplying a colony could not at once be paid for out of the commercial profits of North America, it was necessary to find an objective which would bring in both investors and immediate returns. This was to be found in piracy. While the Queen was still hopeful of finding some basis for peace with Spain, piracy had been, intermittently, frowned on: now that Spanish plots and commercial friction were rapidly wearing down the pretence of good relations, reluctance to countenance piracy was disappearing and the Queen was willing to take shares in it herself. She supplied a ship for Raleigh's expedition, and probably invested money. Sir Francis Walsingham was a subscriber, and Sir Richard Grenville, who led the expedition in 1585, was another. Raleigh's contacts at Court and among the gentry of Devon and Cornwall were sufficient to get him a good deal of help from wealthy people. William Sanderson, a rich London merchant who was married to Raleigh's niece, served as a link with the mercantile community. Thus money was collected for an expedition: it was expected to recoup it, in the main, by the seizure of Spanish ships at sea. It is possible, too, that the offices and perquisites which the Queen continued to give Raleigh were partly to enable him to take a considerable personal share in the venture.

Throughout the autumn and winter of 1584–5 the preparations went on. Raleigh may have aspired to lead the expedition himself, for a Spanish report in February 1585 suggested that the Queen was holding him back by promising to pay his share in the costs if he stayed at home.

Elizabeth did not approve of members of her intimate circle risking their lives on speculative enterprises. But there is no proof that Raleigh intended to go. His part was that of the *entrepreneur* who planned the venture rather than the active participant, and it was important that he should remain in England to organize supplies of men and materials.

It is clear that he did not intend to organize his colony on Gilbert's lines. There is no mention of grants of land to intending settlers. They were intended to work together as paid servants of the investors, under the commander whom Raleigh appointed. Probably, they were promised good wages and a share in profits, but the results of their labours in America were to go to pay the promoters. One effect of this plan was that no printed propaganda to attract investor-settlers was necessary. The personnel of the colony could be recruited from friends, subordinates and servants of the organizers who were anxious for adventurous and profitable service.

The first American colonizing expedition left Plymouth on April 9, 1585, under the command of Sir Richard Grenville. His flagship, the *Tyger*, was adventured by or hired from the Queen, and was accompanied by four ships— *Roebuck*, *Lion*, *Elizabeth* and *Dorothy*—as well as two pinnaces. After making the ocean crossing the fleet passed through the Lesser Antilles

65

early in May, and for more than a month made free of the King of Spain's islands for their own purposes.

Prizes, information and supplies for the colony were what they wanted. On an uninhabited part of Porto Rico, they built a fortified camp, inside which a twenty-ton pinnace, to replace one lost on the voyage, was constructed. Later, Ralph Lane, who was to command the Virginian settlers, went on shore to carry off a store of salt collected by the Spaniards. After taking several prizes, Grenville brought his vessels to Isabella, in Hispaniola, where he traded openly for live-stock—horses, cows, goats, sheep and pigs—for the colony, and for goods for sale in England. He also sought information of Spanish military and naval dispositions, as Drake was planning a further raid on the West Indies. While on shore on these and other islands, seeds, roots and cuttings of edible plants—including sugar-canes—were collected and conserved so that they could be planted in Virginia.

To spend over a month in the West Indies was a luxury which the intending colonists could scarcely afford. Yet the visit was not without value. Fresh water and food for the crews were essential. Prizes were important if the expedition was to pay its way. Salt, livestock and plants could all be invaluable to the colonists.

The mainland of North America was first sighted on June 20 somewhere in the vicinity of Santa Elena, and three days later the ships were endangered by a storm off Cape Fear. The next day they took shelter in a harbour some way north of the cape, possibly at Beaufort Inlet. A party landed to refresh themselves and to fish. They were still too far south to settle. The colony was to be primarily a privateering base for use against the Spanish Indies, but it was also to be a centre for surveying the interior and for carrying out experiments in plantation agriculture, preparatory to full-scale occupation.

Passing Cape Lookout, the ships *Tyger* and *Elizabeth*, two Spanish prizes and the new pinnace (the *Roebuck*, *Lion* and *Dorothy* were already at Hatteras) ran along the coast until they reach a fresh opening at Wococon where the *Tyger* anchored off shore. They tried, three days later, to bring her into the harbour, but had evidently made inadequate soundings, as she struck, grounded and was only re-floated with great difficulty. This was the first of many indications that this was no coast for safe harbours or anchorages.

The greater part of the provisions which were to tide the colonists over the winter, doubly important as it was now too late to sow crops, were damaged when water entered the *Tyger*. The wheat and other provisions went musty and the salt was spoiled. Though Grenville left what he could, Hariot tell us that this amounted only to food for twenty days, and that thereafter they had to live off the country. It is probable

67

that their equipment was none too lavish in any case, since again Hariot says there was 'want of English means for the taking of beasts, fish and fowl. . . . Some want also we had of clothes.' It was not an auspicious beginning.

The early days of July were occupied in sending out exploring parties. A message was sent to Roanoke to inform the chief Wingina of their arrival. John Arundell was sent to the mainland with Manteo, who had taken to English ways. Captains Aubrey and Bonython were despatched to explore Croatoan, the next island up the reef.

On the return of the first reconnaissance parties, Grenville, on July 11, led a more considerable expedition to the mainland. The new pinnace, with three boat-loads of men, passed through the reef into Pamlico Sound. This is how Hariot describes the problems they encountered:

'The sea coasts of Virginia are full of islands whereby the entrance into the main land is hard to find. For although they be separated with divers and sundry large divisions, which seem to yield convenient entrance, yet to our great peril we proved that they were shallow, and full of dangerous flats, and could never pierce up into the mainland, until we made trails, in many places with our small pinnace.'

The party crossed Pamlico Sound, and Grenville saw his first Indian village, Pomeioc, a

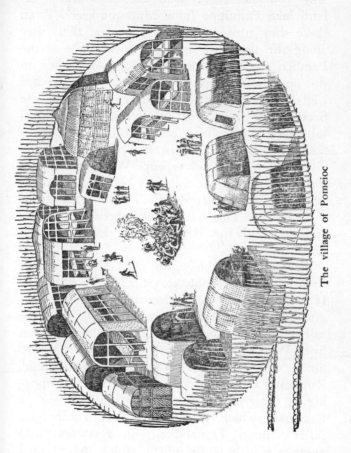

The village of Pomeioc

small palisaded settlement. It was some little way from the shore, near the considerable inland lake Paquippe (now Mattamuskeet). From there they turned south and worked their way along the northern side of the entrance to the Pamlico River, first to Aquascogoc and then to the open settlement of Secoton, a tribal centre well known to us from White's paintings. At Secoton the party was well received and entertained by the Indians, but on their way back a boat was sent to Aquascogoc to demand the return of a stolen silver cup. When it was not forthcoming and the villagers had fled, Amadas and his men destroyed their corn and burnt their houses. This was the first breach with the Indians, and the initiative was taken by the English.

Returning on the eighth day, Grenville and Lane were better able to estimate the situation. It was probably now that it was decided to attempt to establish the colonists on Roanoke rather than on the mainland. The fleet moved from Wococon on July 21, and an attempt was made to find some more suitable harbour. Rounding Cape Hatteras, they reached an opening in the reef, opposite to the southern end of Roanoke, which they called Port Ferdinando (after Simon Fernandez), or Hatteras, and another a little to the north, which they named Trinity Harbour. Both have for long been closed, but the former is near the modern Oregon

Inlet. Neither was really suitable. Port Ferdinando had a good defensive position, but this did not make up for the fact that only the smaller vessels could cross the bar and that the rest had to anchor in the roads.

Two days after the ships had been secured, on July 29, Granganimeo, brother of the Roanoke chieftain and Amadas's old acquaintance, came with Manteo to see Grenville. He probably invited the Englishmen to make the island their headquarters. In any event, it was decided to establish the settlement at the north end of the island, near the Indian village, and the main business of the next few weeks was the discharge of men and goods and the construction of a fort and dwellings. Amadas took a party to investigate Weapemeoc, the Indian territory on the north shore of Albemarle Sound. There was also some trade in skins and furs in exchange for dolls, copper and various metal objects. Specimens of local commodities were collected and reports on natural resources prepared for Raleigh's information. When Grenville returned he had with him, as Lane said, 'a great mass of good things . . . to avoid all suspicion of fraud.'

As cargoes were discharged the ships left for home, between August 5 and September 8 or 9. Lane kept the pinnace and a few boats, but a sizable ship would have given him a more effective mobility, especially when he decided

71

that Roanoke was not, after all, suitable as a permanent site for the colony.

One constant impediment to the conduct of overseas expeditions in Elizabeth's reign was the outbreak of dissensions among the leadership. Many of the men were strong individualists, impatient of discipline and hard to organize, as in Grenville's expedition. Lane and those of the party whose special interest was in America considered that Grenville had wasted time in the West Indies, and this caused friction. Quarrels arose between Lane and Grenville over the detailed conduct of affairs while they were in the West Indies. Grenville also blamed Fernandez for bad pilotage and as responsible for the grounding of the *Tyger*; Lane, on the other hand, became his champion. While the ships lay off the reef Lane gathered a party around him and despatched strongly critical reports to England about Grenville, whom he accused of threatening to have him tried for his life.

We do not know Grenville's own case, and it is not easy to judge between them. Both were proud and intolerant of opposition. Yet Grenville had a difficult task to combine trade in the West Indies and the establishment of a colony in America with sufficient privateering to pay the costs of the voyage, and he did his job successfully. In any case, it is clear that dissensions were taken as a matter of course, so long as they did not bring disasters with them. There was, after all, a certain workmanlike efficiency in Grenville's conduct of the expedition and in Lane's handling of the colony, which compares favourably with the amateurish efforts of John White in 1587 and later years.

On leaving the Roanoke colony on August 25, Grenville, in the *Tyger*, entered the track of the Spanish treasure and merchant fleets bound for Europe. He narrowly missed the *flota* of thirty-three vessels which had left Havana in July. But the *Santa Maria*, a large, unarmed merchantman of 300 tons from San Domingo, lagged behind. Off Bermuda the *Tyger* overhauled her and attacked. She surrendered. The master and passengers were ordered to hand over their jewellery and money. The ship's manifest showed a cargo of gold, silver and pearls, sugar, calf-hides, ginger, cochineal and other articles, to the value of 120,000 ducats. Grenville impounded the bullion and jewels and, transferring half her complement to the *Tyger*, he stayed in her himself with a prize crew. After some dangers, she arrived at Plymouth on October 18, twelve days after the *Tyger* had anchored at Falmouth.

Raleigh hurried down to Plymouth, both to hear the news of the colony and to oversee the valuation and disposal of the cargoes and prize goods. As was usual, the crews endeavoured to seize for themselves what they could. Rumours

73

began to fly around about the great value of the cargo, some estimating it at a million ducats. Six weeks later Grenville assured Walsingham that each adventurer would get his money back 'with some gain,' but that the stories about pearls, gold and silver being on board were false and the value of the ginger and sugar was about 40,000 to 50,000 ducats. This was probably too little, as the Spanish estimate sounds fair. The Queen is said to have taken a whole cabinet of pearls for herself. In addition to the prize cargo there was the ship herself, the two prizes taken in the West Indies and their cargoes, the goods traded in the West Indies, and the goods and specimens brought from Virginia. Whatever the total reckoning, it is clear that the establishment of the first colony did not cost Raleigh anything, and may well have brought him profit sufficient to pay the costs of the reconnaissance of 1584 and some part at least of the supplies despatched in 1586. It also kept his credit high with his fellow-investors.

While Grenville was making his profitable voyage home, Ralph Lane, with his 107 companions, was beginning the construction of the first English colony on American soil. What were he and his associates like? Lane was a solider of over twenty years' service, an expert on fortifications who had been sent to Ireland in 1583 to plan the defence of the south-west coast against Spanish incursions. He later commanded the garrisons in Kerry and part of Limerick, and became sheriff of Kerry. He then became ambitious to take a hand in the plantation of the confiscated lands in this area, but he antagonized his superiors, Sir Henry Wallop, vice-treasurer of Ireland, wrote of him to Burghley that he wanted to rule everything and have the disposal of all the land himself; 'Kerry is too large for Mr. Lane,' he added. It was evidently here that he became interested in colonization, but it was possibly because he had made enemies in Ireland that he embarked on the American enterprise. He was allowed to appoint a deputy 'in consideration of his ready undertaking the voyage to Virginia for Sir Walter Raleigh at Her Majesty's command.' We get a fairly clear picture of his character and abilities while in America. He was energetic, hard-working, practical, reasonably quick and decisive in action, a disciplinarian—all qualities valuable in a leader of pioneers. He took care of his men's health, and was very successful, or lucky, in avoiding sickness among them. On the other hand, he was inclined to grouse and blame his superiors. He knew how to organize a garrison and conduct exploring expeditions, but he had little idea of building up the commercial and agricultural activities on which the permanence of the colony would depend. He treated the problem of relationships with the natives as primarily a military one, in which requisitioning, the taking of hostages and the use of force were natural steps. He could see his way clearly enough to the end of the first stage in the establishment of a colony—the building of a strong, fortified settlement on a suitable harbour. This he considered to be his personal assignment in America, after which he was free to leave. The idea of a diversified community, building up family life on the basis of individual and communal enterprise, was beyond him.

As governor, Lane was virtually dictator over his little company. He tells us that, with Grenville's approval, he had 'set down a discipline which was severely executed, first at sea, and then afterwards by me, in like sort, continued at land.' But, for the effective running of the enterprise, he had to work with the other officers and gentlemen who were under him. He appears to have done so, not without friction, but without any serious crisis. Of his second-in-command, Philip Amadas, 'admiral of Virginia,' we know little, but in practice Lane relied chiefly on Captain Edward Stafford. 'I must truly report of him from the first to the last,' Lane said, 'he was the gentleman that never spared labour or peril either by land or water, fair weather or foul, to perform any service committed unto him.'

Thomas Hariot was the scientific expert of the expedition. A fine mathematician, he was probably in charge of the 'mathematical instru-

ments, sea compasses . . . perspective glass . . .
spring-clocks,' which he tells us so impressed the
Indians. His special task was to collect and
examine the vegetable and mineral products of
the region, to study agricultural and commercial prospects, and to deal with the native
inhabitants. He had considerable powers of
observation, though perhaps his outlook was a
little too academic for immediate needs. Though
optimistic about what he saw as a basis for
future developments, he was not uncritical. He
studied the Indian peoples with loving curiosity,
and was concerned that relations between them
and the settlers should become increasingly close
and friendly. He respected their skill and
capacity within the primitive limits of their
society. He tried to expound Christianity to
them, and believed that in time they could be
converted and civilized. He won and kept the
respect of Lane, who in 1588 commended his
honesty and his learning, and he was clearly
a very valuable influence in the small community.

These three, with twelve other gentlemen,
made up the informal council which Lane consulted. Among them were some drones and
grumblers, gentlemen who expected to be well
looked after whatever happened. Hariot said of
some of them that, as soon as it appeared probable that gold and silver were not to be found
immediately, they 'had little or no care for any

other thing but to pamper their bellies.' He
went on caustically:

'Some also were of a nice bringing up, only
in cities or towns, or such as never (as I may
say) had seen the world before. Because there
were not to be found any English cities, nor
such fair houses, nor at their own wish any of
their old accustomed dainty food, nor any soft
beds of down or feathers, the country was to
them miserable.'

There is no evidence that this element was a
very serious source of discord, but it was unfortunate since, in such a small community under
pioneering conditions, every man was needed to
pull his weight.

Of the rank and file it is probable that the
majority had served some period in the army,
and indeed much of the organization of the
settlers was that of a company of soldiers. There
were several Irishmen among them, brought by
Lane from Kerry, and a number of names which
look German. One of these was a German-
Jewish minerals expert, Joachim Ganz. We
do not hear of any specialized farmers or
gardeners. On the whole, they preserved toler-
able discipline, and showed courage and
endurance on several occasions. Yet they had
little personal stake in the colony, unless some
remarkable discoveries of precious metals were
made. They served for wages under military

discipline, and during the hard winter and spring many thought principally of how soon they would be able to leave America. It is not surprising that their reports when they returned were unfavourable and that they did not wish to return.

One member of the party has been left for special mention—John White. One of the more outstanding artists to go with exploring expeditions into new lands, he had learnt his craft in England as a member of the Painters-Stainers Company. He accompanied Frobisher on at least one of his north-western voyages, that of 1577, and had drawn Eskimos in Baffin Land. He had been with Amadas and Barlow in 1584 and now he had come to record (in association with Hariot) the plants, birds, fish and Indian life of the new Virginia. He had exceptional skill with pencil and brush and did remarkably natural and lively drawings of what he saw.[1]

Twenty-one drawings, three of them now only represented by engravings, of Indian villages, customs, crafts and personalities were made in North Carolina while he was under Lane's command. Together with his copies of two of Le Moyne's Florida Indians, they make up a body of work from which we can derive a very clear impression of the people among whom the colonists passed their time in America, supple-

[1] See British Museum, *Catalogue of British Drawings*, ed. E. Croft-Murray and P. Hulton, I (1960), 26–30.

mented as they are by his own notes and by Hariot's and Lane's descriptions. He worked hand-in-hand with Hariot. For the most part Hariot described and identified species of fish and plants with which he was acquainted in England or had read of in Nicholas Monardes' *Joyfull Newes out of the Newfounde Worlde*, a Spanish account of American products, published in English in 1577. Those which he could not identify certainly or wished to place on record, White painted.

White was also a cartographer. Out of the materials which he collected during his stay he made the first reasonably detailed map of the region covered by the reef and including the entrance to Chesapeake Bay.

To White, even more than to Hariot and Lane, whose detailed narratives have been lost, we owe our knowledge of what the America in which the first colony lived looked like. Like Hariot, he became an enthusiast for America; unlike him, he staked everything on the establishment of a third colony, of which he went as governor.

Roanoke Island provided a useful centre for exploring the sounds and the rivers penetrating the mainland. But, though accessible enough by boat from the best harbour available, it was too limited in area and too thickly inhabited already by the Indians to make a good nucleus for an expanding agricultural community. One of the earliest of Lane's tasks was to build a fort and houses for his men. Unfortunately, White has left us no picture of the result.

The ditch and rampart of the fort were carefully excavated and restored between 1947 and 1953. They show how small the enclosed area was—some seventy feet square. Inside it a building with an upper story was erected to act as store-house, magazine and guardroom. The outer defences were well planned, Lane being a fortifications expert, and they were sited so as to cover possible Spanish approaches, while being concealed from observation by reconnaissance parties on the Outer Banks. The 'town', where houses were run up for the settlers—Hariot, for example, had one —was nearby, and fort and houses were near an Indian village at the north-western tip of the island. The village site has now been washed away. No trace has yet been found of the 'town'.

The appropriation of the land for the fort and houses must have been made by agreement with the Indians, and no attempt was made to enclose and cultivate any appreciable quantity of ground. We do not know how much of the livestock from the West Indies, besides horses, survived the voyage.

The colonists were not good at improvising effective means of feeding themselves. They could not learn the Indian knack of building fish-weirs from reeds, and Hariot complains of their want of

English means for the taking of beasts, fish and fowl.

The many plants and fruits brought from the West Indies, including sugar-canes and plantains, had either perished on the voyage or did not survive transplantation so late in the season. The seed wheat went musty after its immersion when the *Tyger* struck. A few grains of barley, oats and peas grew where they had sown themselves. Nothing, in fact, was done in the autumn of 1585 to attempt to feed the colony from foodstuffs it grew itself. Apart from hunting and collecting, they depended entirely on the Indians for food. In the spring of 1586 they got the Indians to sow some ground specially for them, and also to set aside some cleared ground for them to plant. That this is mentioned by Lane shows that there was no seizure of land without the Indians' assent. Hariot and others had watched carefully the Indian method of cultivating maize, and the sowing was carried through with seed obtained from them. By the middle of June the corn was only a fortnight from ripening. They reckoned that, when they had harvested it and received what the Indians had sown for them, they could survive for two years without further agricultural effort.

Whatever Lane's men might have done had they stayed, there is good ground for agreeing with Dr. Williamson's conclusion[1] that they considered themselves as a military expedition,

[1] J. A. Williamson, *Age of Drake*, pp. 245–6.

'looking for their rations to the commissariat and acting only on the command of their superiors,' and that as such they could not form an effective society to exploit the country and maintain themselves: 'a military force could not grow crops.'

In the first few weeks, while the ships were still with them, the members of the expedition collected goods and specimens and bartered with the Indians with a will. Thereafter most of their trading and collecting had the more immediate purpose of keeping themselves alive. They had some goods collected when they left in June, but probably not much of value, and it is unlikely that they were much better traders than they were farmers.

Lane's first impressions, in the letters he sent from Virginia in August and September 1585, were very favourable. Thus he wrote to Walsingham on August 12:

'That this our present arrival into these parts, though late in the year . . . hath nevertheless discovered unto us so many, so rare and so singular commodities . . . as all the kingdoms . . . of Christendom, their commodities joined in one together, do not yield . . . more good or more plentifully whatsoever for public use is needful or pleasing for delight.'

He continued to be impressed by the potential resources of the area, but he became rather less optimistic about the possibilities of exploiting them; English people would not readily settle where it was difficult to make commodities pay their way. He thought that only if this part of America offered some further attraction would its resources be fully developed. His own words are:

> 'the discovery of a good mine . . . or a passage to the South Sea, or some way to it, and nothing else can bring this country in request to be inhabited by our nation. And with the discovery of either of the two above showed, it will be the most sweet and healthfullest climate, and therewithal the most fertile soil (being manured) in the world: and then will Sassafras, and many other roots and gums there found make good merchandise and lading for shipping, which otherwise of themselves will not be worth the fetching.'

He was unable to envisage a reasonably self-supporting English society rooting itself in America. He clearly did not believe that the growing of Mediterranean fruits would be practicable as a commerical proposition, and he was right when he declared that timber and other bulky exports were hardly sufficient to maintain a colony largely dependent on trade. A colony in this region did need a staple commodity of small bulk and relatively high price. He did not imagine that the tobacco which he and his companions learnt to smoke in Roanoke would provide that staple for a later Virginia.

Thomas Hariot, on the other hand, remained optimistic of developing a colony, even without the spectacular discovery of minerals. He chided those of his companions who had lost interest when gold and silver were not at once discovered. He stressed through his *Briefe and True Report of the New Found Land of Virginia*, which he finished in February 1588, the native plants which could be grown by settlers who were sincerely concerned with getting a living there. The ease with which maize could be cultivated offered of itself great prospects for the survival of a colony. He dealt with such practical problems as how settlers were to build houses in the absence of stone from the coastal area. With imported domestic animals and the cultivation of English seeds and West Indian plants, living would, he thought, be easy. At the same time, he believed it could also be profitable, with settlers producing such a surplus 'as by way of traffic and exchange with our own nation of England will enrich yourselves the providers; those that shall deal with you, the enterprisers in general, and greatly profit our own countrymen, to supply them with most things which heretofore they have been fain to provide either of strangers or of our enemies.'

85

Such were the two views as to future prospects. In general Lane's was, for Elizabethan conditions, the more realistic, Hariot's the more far-sighted.

Lane considered the exploration of the mainland to be the primary task, and after the departure of the ships he prepared to follow up the preliminary reconnaissance of the Pamlico River and Albemarle Sound made during July and August, and to extend inquiries northward towards Chesapeake Bay.

The exploration southwards up the Pamlico River was not pressed with any great vigour and did not lead to any new discoveries. Lane decided to leave further investigation in this area until better-equipped and larger parties should be available the following summer.

The expedition to the north was not led by Lane in person. He tells us that the passage through Currituck Sound, north of the mouth of Albemarle Sound, 'was very shallow and most dangerous.' He tell us, too, that the exploring party penetrated some 130 miles from Roanoke, and finally entered the territory of the Chesapains, whose town, some fifteen miles from the shore, was well situated. The land was very fertile, and the climate, the fishing, the plentiful bears (black bears of the Great Dismal Swamp) and fine timber were attractive. White's map shows a shoal towards the head of Currituck Sound, south of Knotts Island, and a passage through the reef to the north. It would appear that the party crossed by land from somewhere near this point to the village marked 'Chesepuic' (Chesapeake) on the map and situated about ten miles west of Cape Henry. They established themselves there, on Lane's orders, for some considerable time, and were visited by a number of neighbouring Indian chiefs. It is also very probable, from the evidence of the map, that the party worked back to the entrance to the reef by way of Cape Henry. They clearly learnt something of the southern entrance to Chesapeake Bay and of Hampton Roads and the James River from the Indians. On White's map Scicoac is marked as an Indian town near the modern site of Gilmerton, and two unnamed villages are indicated farther to the west, while they received some vague reports of the northern shore. The interest of this expedition, of which we would gladly know more, is twofold. Added to what Lane later heard from the Chowan River Indians, the indications were that this area would be more suitable for a permanent settlement than Roanoke and would provide deep-water harbours for shipping. It was also the first recorded English visit to Virginia proper, the modern state-line reaching the sea just where White marked the final passage through the reef.

Albemarle Sound, with the Chowan and Roanoke Rivers flowing into it, attracted Lane's most serious attention, partly as it offered easy passage 'through a broad sound . . . the channel of great depth,' and partly because the breadth of the opening and the considerable flow of water might indicate a great continuous water-way, comparable with the St. Lawrence, leading far into the interior, possibly to, or near, the Pacific itself.

Amadas had gone up early in August to make the first contact with the Indian tribe which inhabited the many inlets on the northern shore of Albemarle Sound, which Lane reported early in September. It was not, however, until late February or early March that Lane penetrated farther, into the Chowan River, the territory round which was called Chawanoac and its chief Menatonon. This was the largest Indian community he encountered, the main village, Chawanoac, being able to put 700 fighting men into the field. Apparently Lane was nervous of trusting his party against such odds, so he managed in some way to take the chief prisoner and held him for several days, releasing him when he handed over his son as a hostage. The son was kept at Roanoke for several months. Menatonon gave Lane an elaborate account of the countries to the north and west of Chawanoac. He said that three days up the Chowan River and four days overland would bring him to an Indian tribe living by the sea-side, with its base on an island in a bay in deep water. To Lane this story seemed to link up with what he already knew of the Chesapeake and to provide the final justification for moving thither. He planned, therefore, when his expected supplies arrived, to go up the Chowan River with 200 men in boats, picking up guides from Menatonon on the way. Where they indicated that the expedition should leave the river he proposed to place an outpost to guard the boats and proceed overland, leaving a chain of posts behind him to secure his retreat. Once he had reached his objective he would make contact with the small bark and two pinnaces which he intended to send round by sea to test the water route and make soundings. He would then, if everything appeared favourable, construct a fort, to which he 'would have reduced our whole habitation from Roanoke and from the harbour and port there (which by proof is very naught) unto this other beforementioned.' This scheme sounds a little over-elaborate, but it was sensible enough in its final recognition that Roanoke and its surroundings were not suitable for the quick construction of an enduring colony.

Menatonon had things to tell Lane, too, of what he might find if he explored the Roanoke River ('River of Moratuc'), which entered the head of Albemarle Sound from the west. The Mangoak Indians along its upper reaches had plenty of copper, which sounded to Lane like gold. It came from the country of Chaunis

Temoatan, where the 'copper' was panned, almost pure, from a river. Further, he said that, by report, the Roanoke River had its origin some thirty to forty days' journey from its mouth, in a stream of water flowing from a great rock which was itself very near the sea.

These stories thoroughly stimulated Lane, for they offered a prospect of the greatest lure of explorers, gold, and also, to men who knew little or nothing of the vast extent of the interior of North America, the possibility, as alluring as that of gold, of an easy approach to the Pacific. The Roanoke River, it is true, did rise among the great rocks of the Blue Ridge, but very far from any western sea. There was also gold and copper in its basin, and some may well have been won by the Indians, but there was no El Dorado.

Lane had thus two possible future courses of action—to follow the cautious and rational one of transferring his headquarters to the Chesapeake, which he might have done piecemeal without waiting for supplies to arrive, or to follow the will-o'-the-wisp of gold up the Roanoke River. He chose the latter, because it might bring within his grasp untold riches and present the relieving expedition with a marvellous achievement. He released Menatonon and went back to Roanoke. There he prepared two boats for forty men, nearly half his whole company, with some supplies of food, and prepared to set out on his journey, even though relations with the Indians had become threatening.

We have no connected account of the settlers' relations with the Roanoke Indians, but we can infer a certain amount. The chief Wingina, who later changed his name to Pemisapan on the death of his friendly brother Granganimeo, ruled Roanoke and Dasemunkepeuc, on the mainland opposite the island. It was on this small tribe that the settlers mainly depended. They got from the Indians in the harvest season considerable quantities of maize, which formed their staple diet over the winter. The Indians also supplied meat, fish and roots. Doubtless, the colonists did some hunting and collecting on their own account, but not enough for their needs. From the evidence, it would be wrong to suppose that the Indians did not store any of their maize harvest. They evidently kept intact a considerable supply of seed, but during the spring and early summer they became increasingly dependent on hunting, fishing and collecting before their harvest ripened. It was probably at the beginning of this phase that their relations with the settlers became seriously strained, as the latter tended to increase their demands for food and, possibly, to offer increased quantities of copper for it. It is also possible that this pressure was accompanied with violence, for we are told, in one anonymous account, of 'cruelty and outrages committed by some of them against the native inhabitants of that country.' In any event, the Roanoke Indians sharply changed their attitude towards the white men.

The result was that Pemisapan, learning of Lane's intention to explore the Roanoke River, organized his first conspiracy against him. He informed the Albemarle Sound Indians that Lane was coming with a force to attack and destroy them, and drove them into a defensive alliance. He concealed his intentions from Lane, gave him guides, and warned him that there was danger of the Indians up-river joining for an attack on Roanoke.

Lane set off for the Roanoke River in these unpropitious circumstances. Each village he found deserted by the Indians, who had carefully removed their corn and other stores. Consequently, Lane found himself far from his base (he says 160 miles, but this is a considerable exaggeration) with only two days' food in hand. His men agreed to proceed in the hope of obtaining copper (which they thought to be gold) from the Mangoaks. But after two days they were reduced to eating two mastiffs which they had brought with them. In the morning Lane turned back and, travelling rapidly on the swift current, reached Albemarle Sound on Easter Sunday. The Weapemeoc Indians, too, had deserted their villages, but the explorers found enough fish in the weirs to keep them going.

Meantime, on Roanoke, Pemisapan had been carrying on a war of nerves against the sixty-odd men left there. He put out the story that Lane had perished by starvation. He was also preparing to desert Roanoke, leaving his ground there unsown. This would, as Lane said, have meant disaster; 'for at that time we had no weirs for fish, neither could our men skill of the making of them, neither had we one grain of corn for seed to put into the ground.' It is surprising that the Indians did not take more violent measures, but they apparently still feared the magic which the white men could work with their guns.

The return of Lane's party without loss was a severe blow to Pemisapan's theory that the Englishmen could be starved to death. Their three Indian guides bore witness to their strength and prowess, and Ensenore, a friendly elder statesman of the tribe, was able to influence Pemisapan in their favour. Their prestige was further strengthened when Menatonon sent down pearls as a bid to ransom his son and also ordered the chieftain of Weapemeoc to submit himself to Lane as 'servant, and homager, to the great Weroanza [chieftainess] of England, and after her to Sir Walter Raleigh.' It proved possible to get Pemisapan to sow enough corn to keep the colonists supplied for a year, and to hand over enough cleared ground, with seed, to allow them to sow a comparable amount for themselves, while he also had fish-weirs built for them.

They seemed to have surmounted their gravest peril, since within three months they would have enough food even should no reinforcements arrive. The Indian danger, however, was not banished. Ensenore died at the end of April, and Pemisapan began plotting again. He proposed to call together a great confederation of Indians from the mainland. Pemisapan could offer them copper in which, as a result of his trade with the settlers, he was now rich, and also the prospect of further spoil. The allies were to assemble on June 10 at Dasemunkepeuc for the final assault. In the meantime, Pemisapan determined to wear down the colonists by depriving them of food and causing them to disperse into small parties. When this was done the Indians proposed to set on Lane, Hariot and others in their houses, to launch a general attack on the fort and to pick off the scattered groups at leisure.

The first stage of this plan was put into effect. Pemisapan withdrew to the mainland. He ordered that no corn or other provision was to be sold to the English and that their fish-weirs should be robbed and broken. The result of these tactics was that the settlers were threatened with a serious food-shortage and Lane was forced to resort to a policy of dispersal. Captain Stafford with one party was sent to Croatoan to feed himself and look out for shipping. Prideaux, with another, went with the pinnace to the harbour at Port Ferdinando. Each week Lane had to send parties to the mainland to live off cassava and oysters, while the remainder spent much time foraging for crabs and fish.

Yet Lane was able, gradually, to discover the plans of his adversary. Skiko, Menatonon's son, who was taken into Pemisapan's confidence as a presumed enemy of Lane, gave the settlers information. When Pemisapan had assembled his own men on the mainland and was proposing to make an ostensibly friendly visit to Lane, the latter decided to take the initiative. He planned on the night of May 31 to seize their canoes and to surprise the Indians on the island. The plan miscarried, as the seizure of the canoes, which involved the killing of several Indians, was observed. There was a brisk fight and the Indians, after some casualties, fled into the woods. The next morning Lane made his way to the mainland, with only twenty-seven companions, where he arranged to meet Pemisapan on the excuse that he wanted some food to take with him to Croatoan. When the chief and his principal followers met them, Lane gave a signal to his followers who set on the Indians and killed a number of them. Pemisapan, wounded, feigned death and then attempted to escape, but Edward Nugent, one of Lane's Irish soldiers, killed him.

95

Thus plot was met with counterplot and treachery with treachery. Lane's daring apparently cowed the mass of the Indians, and the success of his ruse removed all immediate danger. Yet few of his men can have felt at all secure in those early days of June 1586. Certainly many illusions had been shattered on both sides. The settlers had been acceptable as temporary god-like visitors in 1585; by 1586 they had become men who threatened the security of the Indian society and aroused savage cupidity by their wealth. Lane awaited reinforcements eagerly; instead, he was obliged by circumstances to desert his American outpost.

Chapter Four

Lost Colonies

THE end of Lane's colony came in a way typical of weak organization at home and vulnerability to accident in America. A former Secretary of State to Elizabeth, Sir Thomas Smith, had described young colonies as 'weak and new planted things,' and certainly the first American colony had little strength in it. Its continuance probably, and its development certainly, depended on the early arrival of supplies and reinforcements. It had been arranged that these should arrive in April 1586. Raleigh took the greatest care to make adequate preparations to send supplies, as he knew they were vital for the colony's security. First, there was to be a single vessel of 100 tons, 'freighted,' we are told, by Sir Walter Raleigh, 'with all manner of things in most plentiful manner, for the supply and relief of his colony then remaining in Virginia.' Though he began its equipment in November 1585, it did not leave until after Easter 1586, and it had not reached Port Ferdinando by June 19. A more formidable reinforcement, in men as well as equipment, was to be brought over by Grenville. His fly-boat, with

97

some other vessels, attempted to leave harbour on April 16, but one of the ships grounded on Bideford Bar and this meant further delay. They did not reach Port Ferdinando until about mid-July. Both reliefs were too late. The colonists had gone home with Drake, Raleigh's ship missing them by a few days and Grenville's fleet by about a month.

That the means to leave were at hand was hardly fortuitous. The year 1585 had seen the despatch of other and more imposing expeditions directed against Spanish power overseas. A temporary arrest of English shipping in Spanish ports in May provided an excuse for carrying out an old project of Sir Humphrey Gilbert. Raleigh 'was directed to set forth certain ships for interrupting such of the King of Spain's subjects . . . as should repair to the fishing at Newfoundland.' He diverted Virginia-bound Bernard Drake of Ash, a relative of Sir Francis, who was to instruct English fishermen on the Newfoundland Banks to take no catches to Spain or Portugal, and to seize Spanish and Portuguese fishing-vessels. Drake's voyage was successful and he made a large haul of ships and men, but he died in April 1586 of fever caught from the prisoners he had packed into Exeter gaol. Meantime, Sir Francis Drake had left Plymouth in September 1585 with a formidable fleet of twenty-nine vessels, containing 2,300 soldiers and sailors. Of the £60,000 invested in the enter-

prise, the Queen's adventure amounted to
£20,000 and Raleigh also participated. Its
avowed objectives were to capture or destroy as
much Spanish shipping as possible and to inflict
the maximum damage on the Spanish ports
in America. Whether the Queen knew and
approved or not, there was another objective,
to seize a base in the Spanish Indies—Drake
favoured Cartagena—as a preliminary to an
attempt to conquer the Spanish empire. Sir
Philip Sidney hoped to lead the force which
would begin this great adventure, but the Queen
prevented him from leaving the country and the
military command fell to Christopher Carleill,
Walsingham's stepson and an enthusiast for
colonization in North America. It is not fanciful
to see in the three-fold move against Spain in
1585—Drake's expedition, the Newfoundland
exploit and the Virginia colony—the component
parts of a new aggressive strategy against the
Spanish empire. The limited achievements of
Drake and Lane, with events in Europe, may
account for the failure to follow it up in suc-
ceeding years.

Drake's exploits were spectacular enough,
sacking and ransoming both San Domingo and
Cartagena, and inflicting a considerable blow on
Spanish military and naval power. The deple-
tion of his troops by sickness, however, ended the
plan to garrison Cartagena. Drake sailed out of
the Caribbean by way of the Florida Channel,

and launched, at the end of May 1586, a strong attack on St. Augustine, which was destroyed and the remnants of its garrison driven into the interior. Absence of a suitable pilot alone saved Santa Elena from a similar fate. Though St. Augustine was rebuilt in time, the outpost at Santa Elena was withdrawn as the result of Drake's assault. It seems probable that the crippling of the Florida colony had been concerted by Drake with Raleigh before he left England. It was highly desirable from the point of view of the English settlement farther north.

The fleet then sailed on to make contact with Lane's colonists, another move which may have been planned the previous year, for Drake may have wished to see if the settlement would make a good base for an attack on the treasure fleet. Off Croatoan a watch-fire maintained by Captain Stafford's party was sighted on June 9 (Stafford had already seen the ships the previous day and had sent off a messenger to Roanoke). Drake sent off a boat to pick up the watchers, and under their pilotage the fleet proceeded to Port Ferdinando. Only the smaller vessels could take refuge in the bad harbour, the rest had to stand some two miles out in the roads. Stafford, in the meantime, had gone ahead with a letter from Drake to Lane, offering food, arms and clothing, together with ships and boats and men to man them. Lane came at once to the harbour and saw Drake on June 11, when the offer was repeated

and made specific. He wanted Drake to relieve
him of a number of weak and unfit men and to
replace them by oarsmen and craftsmen. He also
gladly accepted the offer of shipping, which
would make it possible for him to move the
settlement to Chesapeake Bay and also give him
the means of returning to England if or when
necessary.

It was arranged that the seventy-ton *Francis*,
capable of using the existing harbour, should be
turned over to Lane, together with boats, navi-
gators, sailors, and food and equipment for 100
men for four months. A number of Lane's men
went on board the *Francis* to take over, and stores
were being transhipped. Then, on June 13, a
fierce thunderstorm, accompanied by waterspouts, burst. It raged for nearly four days.
Cables and anchors snapped, pinnaces and boats
were smashed, and the ships had the greatest
difficulty in escaping disaster. All did, but when
the storm cleared on June 16 the *Francis* was
seen to be setting course for England with some
of the more responsible colonists and many stores
on board. It is legitimate to deduce that her
crew preferred returning to England to enjoy
the spoils of the West Indies expedition to com-
pulsory service in Virginia under Lane.

Drake and Lane were now in a dilemma. Yet
Drake at once showed the sincerity of his desire
to help the colony by offering another vessel, the
Bark Bonner, with such sailors and stores as he

101

could still spare. This ship, of 170 tons, had less
attraction for Lane. She could not be brought
into harbour and might well be too large for
exploring Chesapeake Bay. In any case, nerves
were frayed and confidence shattered. Lane
called a hurried meeting of colonists, and found
that their willingness to persevere had
evaporated. They pointed to their depleted
numbers, to the unsuitability of the *Bark
Bonner*, to the tales of Drake's men that Grenville would not be able to come with supplies
on account of great events looming up in
Europe, and to the carrying off of the *Francis*
'by the very hand of God, as it seemed, stretched
out to take us from thence.' Lane accepted their
decision, and they put their request in writing
to avoid any unpleasantness for Drake with
Raleigh.

The sailors were by this time fretting at the
delay, so pinnaces were rushed to Roanoke to
take off the remainder of the colonists and their
baggage. There was something of a stampede by
sailors and settlers alike to get away from the
treacherous shore. Boats grounded in the shallow
and choppy waters of the Sound. Some things
were upset into the water; others the sailors
hurled away—strings of pearls, maps, books,
detailed accounts of the colony's story, probably
many specimens and some merchandise perished.
Three of the colonists who had gone up country
were left behind. The fleet put to sea on June

18 or 19, and the colonists landed at Portsmouth on July 27.

It is interesting to compare the reactions of one of Drake's soldiers to Florida and Virginia respectively. Florida attracted him: "Here is as goodly a soil as may be, with so great abundance of sweet woods, etc., as is wonderful, with goodly meadows, and store of fish, oysters and mussels, with deer and goodly fields of corn after their manner.' As for the Indians—'for the tag of a point, a bell, a counter, a pin or such like they will give you anything they have.' Of Virginia he had little to say and that not very complimentary: 'This country is indifferently fruitful, and hath good store of fish with land turtles and nice fruits and saxifrage, which are the best things in all the land that we know of.' Most of Lane's company were, when they returned, considerably more uncomplimentary, while Drake, if he had cherished any hope of using an American harbour for attacks on the plate-fleet, was certainly disillusioned about the anchorage he had to choose.

Raleigh's relief ship arrived just too late. Its company, 'after some time spent in seeking our colony up in the country, and not finding them, returned with all the provision into England.' Hard on this vessel's departure Grenville appeared, to find neither Raleigh's ship nor the settlers. He spent some time in the area, 'himself travelling up into divers places of the country, as well to see if he could hear any news of the colony . . . as also to discover some places of the country.' He could get no information whatever of what had happened to Lane, finding only the deserted fort and houses. This is very surprising. The Indians knew very well that Lane had gone. Perhaps Grenville had no interpreters, perhaps the Indians kept severely out of his way, or they may merely have maintained a conspiracy of silence, not wishing to be troubled further by the white men.

His decision was that something must be done to retain possession of the country, and consequently he determined to leave some men behind, 'whereupon he landed fifteen men in the Isle of Roanoke, furnished plentifully with all manner of provisions for two years, and so departed.' This was a fatal half-measure. He had many more settlers than those he left amongst his seven or eight ships. He could not know, of course, how relations between the Indians and Lane's men had deteriorated. But if Lane had the greatest difficulty in preserving his hundred men against Indian attacks, a mere handful had no chance, or only a ghost of a chance, of survival.

What happened to them, in fact, was very much what could have been anticipated. The Indians conspired to destroy the little colony. They sent a party of thirty braves to the island, who landed unobserved. All but two hid, but these invited two of the eleven Englishmen they saw to parley unarmed. Unsuspecting, they left their comrades and were set upon. One was killed, the other managed to rejoin his party. The Indians broke cover and pursued the Englishmen to their headquarters, where they had their food and weapons, and succeeded in setting fire to it. The settlers made a bid to reach their boat. There was a sharp skirmish in the woods, each side having one fatal casualty, and some of the whites also being wounded. The nine survivors managed to get to their boat and to put to sea. On their way they saw the four absent members of their party oyster-catching in a nearby creek, put back and took them on board. They then proceeded to a little island in the reef at the entrance to Port Ferdinando where they established themselves for a time, but eventually moved away. They were never seen again.

Grenville had an arduous voyage. From the Azores he had to take his sick men to Newfoundland to recuperate, and then sailed back to the Islands. But it paid him. To four prizes taken on the way out he added two more, one a ship from Porto Rico with a cargo of sugar, ginger and hides. Back at Bideford in December, he had gone far towards paying for the expedition. On the whole, however, the year had been a bad one for Raleigh. The first colony had returned and the second was a mere holding party. The financing of colonization out of privateering profits was also becoming a less attractive proposition. Now that speculators were convinced of the probability of quick and easy profits out of privateering alone, they were less inclined to venture part of their investment on the still-unproven prospects of colonization. It would not again be easy for Raleigh to get such assistance as he had had before. He had already been refused a subscription by Exeter merchants the previous January.

Again, Lane's settlers had returned in a bad mood. The men had many hardships and obstacles to remember, and the majority of them went about denouncing the promoters, criticizing the conduct of the settlement and crying down the country in which they had lived. Experience convinced Raleigh that his ideas of organizing a colony must be altered. The semi-military community serving the promoters for wages had proved unfit to grow or even survive. On the other hand, Lane, Hariot and White returned enthusiastic 'Americans,' and William Sanderson was willing to continue his financial backing. From Paris, Hakluyt continued to urge that the venture be continued on Chesapeake Bay and to give publicity on the Continent to what had already been achieved. Raleigh decided, therefore, to continue the experiments on a new basis.

The essence of the scheme worked out at the end of 1586 was that the intending shareholders in the third colony should be largely drawn from those who were themselves prepared to go to America. The colonists would get 500 acres on the strength of undertaking to go, and more in proportion to their investment; they would bring out their families to work the farms and build up a continuing community. Organized as a company enjoying rights of self-government under their own officials, they would leave representatives behind in England to employ part of their investment in keeping them supplied until they could maintain themselves in America. This was a much more hopeful arrangement.

Raleigh selected the first governor of the new colony-company and his twelve assistants. White was governor and only he and Simon Fernandez had been there before. Little or nothing is known of the others—Roger Baylye, Ananias Dare, Christopher Cooper, John Sampson, Thomas Steevens, William Fulwood, Roger Prat, Dionise Harvie, John Nichols, George Howe and James Plat. On January 7, 1587, they were given a charter by Raleigh as the 'Governor and Assistants of the City of Raleigh in Virginia,' and were authorized to take out colonists and to exercise certain powers of self-government. This delegation of authority meant neither that Raleigh relinquished ultimate control over the settlers nor that he ceased to contribute his own money for the establishment of the colony. It did mean that colonization was not to be carried on in future by a privateering syndicate with the colonists merely paid servants of promoters sitting in England. They would now have a real stake in the colony.

An expedition was prepared at the beginning of 1587, and 150 colonists were found willing to make the journey and, some of them, to risk their wives and children in the new settlement. Unfortunately, we still know only a little about them, their social origins or their reasons for going to America. But, apart from White, they included only three members of Lane's colony. It may reasonably be inferred that they comprised people of some property, possibly farmers and tradesmen, who realized their possessions in England to equip themselves for the voyage.

Three ships set out to bring the settlers to Virginia. John White was himself captain of the *Lion*, with Fernandez, now one of the assistants in the new company, as master. Most of the colonists were in her, the remainder being in the flyboat or in Captain Edward Stafford's pinnace. The master of the fly-boat, Edward Spicer, was making his first run to America. It was not until May 8 that the vessels cleared for Virginia. The late start was not a good augury.

The expedition bore written instructions from Raleigh. After going to the West Indies for water and to collect plants and livestock for the colony, they were to sail to Roanoke. There they were to embark the fifteen men left by Grenville in

1586. Manteo, the Indian who had returned to England with Lane and whose loyalty had been proved during the conspiracy of Pemisapan, was to be installed at Roanoke as Raleigh's representative. He was willing to become a Christian and he was to be made lord of Roanoke and Dasemunkepeuc. The expedition was then to proceed to Chesapeake Bay and establish there a fort and settlement, which Lane had originally planned, as the City of Raleigh.

We have only White's journal of the voyage— a depressing record. There was continuous friction between White and Fernandez and, if White is to be believed, the latter was guilty of continuous sabotage. The *Lion* and the pinnace made the crossing to the West Indies in five weeks, with the fly-boat two days behind. In the West Indies there followed a weary procession from island to island in search of water and salt, of cattle, fruit and plants, with Fernandez apparently frustrating all their efforts to land at appropriate places or to trade with the Spaniards.

On July 5 they set off for Virginia. The mainland was sighted on July 16. The ships anchored and Fernandez said they were off Croatoan, but after several days admitted he was mistaken. In fact, they were still south of Cape Fear. Moving on, the vessels were nearly wrecked on Cape Fear, owing to 'the carelessness and ignorance of our master,' and were saved by

109

Captain Stafford keeping a good look-out. Finally, the two vessels anchored at the old harbour of Hatteras (Port Ferdinando) on 22 July.

The constant complaints which White brings against Fernandez are not entirely convincing. White was not used to commanding men, and appears, in action, as a weak character. Fernandez, on the other hand, emerges in White's account as bad-tempered, untruthful, inefficient and probably vindicative and treacherous. Why he should have wished to jeopardize the safety of an expedition in which he was a leading shareholder is far from clear. We may, however, guess with some confidence at one major cause of friction. White disliked privateering, and would not risk the lives of women and children in conflicts with Spanish vessels. Fernandez had been a pirate long before the trade had become respectable, and he must have urged the continuance of Grenville's tactics of 1585 to provide some immediate return for the expenditure on the expedition. On this assumption, his actions become partly intelligible. If White would not agree to attacks on Spanish vessels, then, in his turn, he would not assist the colonists to get supplies in the West Indies. But in the absence of more evidence, we cannot be certain that this was the case. Fernandez did not himself intend to remain in America.

On arrival at the reef, White equipped the

pinnace with forty of his best men to sail to
Roanoke. When they had put off from the *Lion*,
they were hailed with a message from Fernandez.
This conveyed the startling news that he had
instructed the sailors to put the colonists on
shore at Roanoke and leave them there. White's
forty men were to be left on the island, and only
White and two or three others allowed to return
to the *Lion* to arrange for the transfer of the
remainder. Fernandez's authority over the sailors
was evidently complete, the pretext being that it
was too late to make for the Chesapeake. White
did not make any effective resistance: 'it booted
not the governor to contend with them,' he said.
Though he was evidently annoyed, the prospect
may not have been altogether displeasing to him.
He knew Roanoke and the surrounding area
well and, unlike Lane, had returned in 1586
very optimistic. The Chesapeake, on the other
hand, was a new venture, involving unknown
dangers.

Once agreement was reached that the settlers
should stay, White went on to Roanoke. There
he found no survivors of the holding party.
Lane's fort had been razed to the ground, but
all the houses nearby were intact, though the
lower rooms were already being invaded by
vegetation. From White's account, it would
appear that the Indian village had been deserted
and the island abandoned by the natives.

He set his men at once to repair the old dwellings and to build new cottages, evidently optimistic that the fly-boat, which had separated from the *Lion*, would arrive with the rest of the planters. His optimism was justified, for, on July 25, she appeared with her complement safe. Her arrival evidently put heart into the preparations, though the dangers from the Indians were illustrated when a raiding-party from the mainland found one of the assistants, George Howe, catching crabs some distance from his companions, and killed him.

On July 30 Stafford took a party of twenty, with Manteo, to Croatoan. The Indian had relatives there, and soon friendly relations were established. The Croatoans explained that they had little maize and extracted a promise that it would not be interfered with. This is a sad commentary on Lane's relations with the Indians. The white man was feared as a stealer of corn. Here the story of the second colony was heard, ending with the disappearance of the thirteen survivors and their boat.

White was anxious to put relations with the mainland Indians on some regular basis, so he got the Croatoans to agree to invite the mainland chiefs and elders to come to Roanoke for a conference within seven days. By August 8 none of them had arrived, so White, who had meantime learnt that it was the Dasemunkepeuc Indians of Pemisapan's tribe who had attacked Grenville's men and had killed Howe, determined to go on shore and destroy their village in revenge. Early in the morning he and his men got behind the village, where they saw a fire and figures moving about. One of the Indians was shot, but another recognized Captain Stafford and managed to convince him that they were a friendly party from Croatoan. They had heard that the village had been deserted, and they had come to gather corn, beans, pumpkins and tobacco. There was some difficulty in explaining the attack, but eventually the Croatoans accepted White's apologies, and his men went back to Roanoke with part of the spoils. There two little ceremonies were held in the days following. On August 13 Manteo was christened and formally installed as Raleigh's vassal in the lordship of Roanoke and Dasemunkepeuc. Five days later, White's daughter Eleanor, who was married to Ananias Dare, one of the assistants, had a daughter. This first English child to be born in America was christened Virginia on the Sunday following.

By about August 20 the little company was settled in. Their chests of clothes and goods, including three of White's containing his books, maps, pictures and armour, had been brought on shore, along with food and other supplies for a year, as well as some artillery designed for the Chesapeake fort. Timber had been cut for sale in England, water had been put on board, and the vessels had been newly caulked and trimmed.

The colonists were writing home. However, while many of the sailors were still on land a severe gale blew the ships off-shore. The *Lion* was unable to return to the roads until August 27.

In the meantime the governor, assistants and company on shore had been disagreeing. Nine of the twelve assistants, including Fernandez, had sailed with White. The three left behind, William Fulwood, John Nichols and James Plat, had probably been assigned the task of preparing supplies to be sent to the colony. But those now with White were apprehensive for the future of the colony. There was little confidence in the Roanoke site. Livestock and salt were lacking, and other deficiencies in stores had become apparent. They wished to send two of their number back to England to expedite a new supply. Christopher Cooper was first persuaded by White to agree to go and then backed out. The cause of the reluctance of the others is not clear. Dare and Harvie would not have wished to leave their wives and children. The remainder may have felt that the responsibility was too great or else they were too optimistic about their American prospects.

On August 22 the assistants and planters urgently requested White to go. They probably felt that he was the best man to take on the organization at the English end, while the presence of his daughter and grandchild in Vir-

ginia would keep him from neglecting the
colony's interests. He urged that his return
would discredit him, and that in any case all his
possessions in Roanoke would be spoiled or
stolen. The company assured him that his goods
would be cared for, and gave him a certificate,
dated August 25, asserting that in spite of his
reluctance he had been chosen by them all to
procure 'the present and speedy supply of certain
our known and apparent lacks and needs most
requisite and necessary for the good planting of
us, or any other, in this land of Virginia.' White
hurried to the harbour and boarded the fly-boat
just before its crew weighed anchor. A mishap
to the capstan caused serious casualties to the
very small crew of fifteen, and left the vessel ill-
equipped for the ocean crossing.

On Roanoke White left eighty-four men,
seventeen women and eleven children, with two
Indians, Manteo and Towaye, who had come
with him from England. They established themselves firmly there, building 'a high palisade of
great trees, with curtains and flankers, very fort-
like' round their dwellings. White left them
with the understanding that 'they intended to
remove fifty miles farther up into the mainland
presently.' Where this objective was we cannot
say definitely. Possibly it was to the vicinity of
the village of Chesapeake at the opening into
Chesapeake Bay, or else it was up Albemarle
Sound, where Lane had, in 1585, remarked on

the fertility of the soil. The pinnace and some boats were left with them.

At some point the colony moved from Roanoke, taking down their houses, but leaving the palisade intact. They buried some chests of goods which they could not take with them in a ditch belonging to the fortifications constructed by Lane and Amadas, and they left behind some heavy cannon and shot. This suggests that they intended to go some distance, and could not easily return for what they could not bring on the pinnace and boats. They did take falcons and other small cannon. They left carved on one tree the letters C R O, and on another, at the entrance to the palisade, C R O A T O A N, as a guide to their immediate destination, without any cross appended, a sign agreed with White to signify a move made under duress or in distress. Whether they stayed on Croatoan with Manteo and his friends cannot be ascertained. They pass out of history, if not from the field of historical speculation. Some seem to have been killed by Powhatan at Chesapeake; others were perhaps absorbed in the Croatoan and Chawanoac Indian tribes, others again maybe lost at sea in their small pinnace. We may never know their final end.

The *Lion* parted company with the fly-boat on September 17 and went seeking prizes. The fly-boat limped back, lacking men and water. She just made Smerwick on the Kerry coast,

White getting shipping to Cornwall, which he reached on November 5. The *Lion* had arrived prizeless at Portsmouth some three weeks before.

Richard Hakluyt was on the point of dedicating to Raleigh the English version of Laudonnière's Florida voyages when he heard of the *Lion's* return with 'good news' for Raleigh 'of the safe arrival of your last colony in their wished haven,' even if the haven was not the one to which the settlers had been directed. Hakluyt worked in a piece of advertising for further expeditions, expressing the belief that when they heard of the riches of Florida from the French narrative many soldiers of fortune would be only too glad to go to Virginia to fight 'against such stubborn savages as shall refuse obedience to her majesty'—indicating that for him at least the Indians had lost their charm of innocence.

Thomas Hariot too was preparing his *Briefe and True Report*, with an introductory letter by Lane, which he finished in February 1588. Hariot, as we have seen, attacked the fainthearted and foolish members of Lane's colony, who had attempted to decry the joys of colonization and the resources of Virginia, and concluded his account of the products of the region with a boost for the third colony and its successors. Raleigh's liberal land-grants to the settlers were praised, and Hariot declared that those who went to America well supplied for a year and used the requisite 'diligence and care' could

RALEIGH AND BRITISH EMPIRE

live well on native produce, get English livestock and grow English crops, and, shortly, 'both
enrich themselves, as also others that shall deal
with them.'

John White, however, had come to stir up
the investors in the third colony to prepare supplies and to beg Raleigh to use all his influence
to hasten them. On receiving from White
written and verbal reports on the situation,
Raleigh decided to act at once. In White's own
words: 'He forthwith appointed a pinnace to
be sent thither with all such necessaries as he
understood they stood in need of: and also wrote
his letters unto them, wherein among other
matters he comforted them with promise, that
with all convenient speed he would prepare a
good supply of shipping and men with suffi-
ciency of all things needful, which he intended,
God willing, should be with them the summer
following.'

Preparations were certainly put in hand immediately, but the pinnace did not manage to sail
during the winter or early spring. It was probably decided that she should set out with the
main supply fleet in April, but endeavour to
make a faster and more direct crossing ahead of
the other ships. The organization and leadership
of the expedition was again entrusted to Grenville. At Bideford he collected ships, including
the *Tyger*, which may have been hired from the
Queen or adventured by her as a sign of her

continued support for the colony. He was almost ready at the end of March 1588, when the Privy Council intervened and commanded Grenville 'to forebear to go his intended voyage' and to hold his ships ready to join the royal fleet for defence against the now seriously threatening *armada*. Grenville, with White entreating him to do so, appealed that some ships should be allowed to go, and he was authorized to send those vessels not required for service. White was thus able to set out on April 22 in the two pinnaces, the *Brave*, thirty tons, and the *Roe*, twenty-five tons, 'with fifteen planters and all their provision, with certain relief for those that wintered in the country.'

Once again White was unlucky. The crews began attacking and boarding merchant ships, irrespective of their nationality. Finally the *Roe*, in which White was, was attacked by a French privateer, damaged and stripped, and had to turn back. 'By this occasion,' said White, 'God justly punishing our former thievery of our evil-disposed mariners, we were of force constrained to break off our voyage intended for the relief of our colony.' The vessel staggered back to the Bristol Channel, and entered Bideford on May 22, just a month after she had set out. A few weeks later the other pinnace also put back to port 'without performing our intended voyage for the relief of the planters in Virginia, which thereby were not a little distressed.'

No one could do more for White or for the colonists in that eventful year. The *armada* came and went in July, and the energies of all Elizabeth's servants and subjects were absorbed in tracking down its survivors. But as the skies began to clear a little at the beginning of 1589, Raleigh did what he could. William Sanderson, Raleigh's friend and man of business, had, we are told, invested over £1,000 in the Virginia colony, and he was prepared to try to save the colony from wreck. The younger Richard Hakluyt had returned from France at the end of 1588, and was also anxious to help. Finally, at the beginning of 1589, a group of nineteen men was got together, who undertook to sponsor the colony and become a sort of holding company for the settlers. They were mainly London merchants: Thomas Smythe, Customer of London, whose son, also Thomas, was later to take a large part in founding the East India Company and Jacobean Virginia; Richard Wright, his son's assistant in the flotation and running of trading companies, and Thomas Hood, the mathematical lecturer who was one of his protégés, made up one important group. William Sanderson and Hakluyt acted as links with Raleigh. Under a deed of March 7, 1589, they were to be made free of the corporation of the City of Raleigh,[1] to share the rights of White's

[1] In 'Affamacomock [elsewhere 'Ossomocomuck'], alias Wingandacoia, alias Virginia.'

group in establishing a settlement and to have freedom of trade without any taxes or customs for all time within the territories colonized under Raleigh's patent. Raleigh reserved to himself and his heirs one-fifth of the profits of gold and silver found in the colony to be established by the corporation, for which he promised to try to obtain a royal charter. As an earnest of his goodwill, he presented them with £100, out of his 'zeal of planting the Christian religion, in, and amongst, the said barbarous and heathen countries.'

Raleigh was trying to ensure that there should be a continuing corporation of wealthy men behind the settlement which White had led to Virginia. He retained his overlordship and a general responsibility for their doings, but was delegating the actual task to them. He did not, of course, surrender his right to sponsor further colonies on other parts of the American coast.

It was White's job to get the reconstructed company to send the requisite reliefs, but little or nothing materialized except for Sanderson's purchase of a ship. Probably the difficulty was seamen. Not only were there great calls on them for national purposes, but everyone who could put to sea preferred privateering to any less spectacularly profitable venture. Thus for nearly a year White continued to be 'troublesome' to Raleigh, 'for the supplies and reliefs of the planters in Virginia.' It was not until early in 1590 that he got his chance.

If action languished, publicity increased. At the end of 1589 Richard Hakluyt completed his great collection of voyages and travels. *The Principall Navigations of the English Nation*, published at the beginning of 1590 with almost all the accounts of the Virginia colonies which have formed the basis for this narrative. Hakluyt thought the best propaganda for colonization was to make public what had been done and what mistakes had been made. A few months later, at Frankfort-on-Main in Germany, appeared another publication, the first part of de Bry's *America*, in four languages—English, Latin, French and German. Theodore de Bry had recently visited England, and there collected Hariot's little book and also twenty-three of White's maps and pictures, with his notes on them, for publication. Thus, shortly before John White was able to make his last effort to find the lost colony, engravings of his pictures were published throughout Europe, and the story of the Virginia enterprises was, unforgettably, put on record.

White's last voyage forms an appendix to this story. In February 1590 all merchant shipping was confined to port as a fresh Spanish attack was feared. This embargo held back three ships belonging to the London privateering merchant, John Watts, the *Hopewell*, *Little John* and *John Evangelist*, destined for the West Indies. Raleigh, through William Sanderson, at White's insistence, got permission for the ships to leave if they took John White to Roanoke Island. Captain Abraham Cocke of the *Hopewell* interpreted the agreement literally, to bring White without supplies or help. This was not as bad as it seems since Sanderson had his *Moonlight*, with Edward Spicer in command, and no doubt well stocked, almost ready to follow. (She did indeed catch up at Cuba in July.)

When White came to Plymouth, therefore, with his companions and their supplies. Captain Cocke and the rest refused to let anyone come aboard except White. As he could not get in touch with Raleigh before the ships put to sea, White accepted these terms. From March 20 to the end of July, the vessels ranged the West Indies, picking up new consorts as well as prizes in their progress. Finally, the *Hopewell*, with White, and the *Moonlight* made for Virginia. They ran into thunder, rain and waterspouts off the Florida coast, which continued until they were off North Carolina. On August 15 they anchored off the old harbour at Port Ferdinando. Sighting smoke from the direction of Roanoke, their hopes of finding the colony were raised, and Captains Cocke and Spicer accompanied White in two boats through the reef towards Roanoke.

Cocke's boat passed safely through the reef

123

in a sharp north-easterly wind, but Spicer's boat overturned, and the captain and six of his men were drowned. This disaster made the men unwilling to go ashore and they urged that the attempt to find the planters be abandoned, but Cocke and White got the overturned boat righted and induced the survivors to re-embark. It was dark when they got to the north end of the island, but they saw a fire through the trees and, anchoring for the night, sounded trumpet calls and 'many familiar English tunes of songs' without result. In the morning they found the fire to be only grass and rotten trees, apparently set on fire by the sun. They worked through the woods to the shoreward side of the island, opposite Dasemunkepeuc, and thence to the site of the settlement. What they found there has already been described—the houses gone and a new palisade in position, some cannon and metal in the grass, and the signs indicating departure to Croatoan. The sailors, rummaging round, found five chests, which had been hidden in the old ditch. White found three were his, his books, maps and pictures torn and his armour rusted. All had been looted by the Indians. White was not discouraged. He envisaged the settlers comfortably established with Manteo on Croatoan.

After a stormy night, Captain Cocke proposed to move on and search Croatoan, but he lost all his anchors except one in trying to clear from the anchorage. The *Hopewell* was thus in a bad way, and White agreed that they had best run for the West Indies and return in the spring. The *Moonlight* was sent off to England, but the *Hopewell*, too, was blown off her course, and her captain took her home. So finally White returned for the last time from Virginia on October 24. He could bear no more misfortune and, getting no support for further expeditions, he decided to 'leave off from prosecuting that whereunto I would to God my wealth were answerable to my will.' The last we know of him is when on February 4, 1593, he wrote to tell Hakluyt something of his fifth and last voyage to Virginia. Certainly his persistence was admirable, but one gets the impression that his abilities, apart from his painting and map-making were mediocre. After White, there is no certain record of any attempt to seek for the lost colony or to send out any further settlers until 1602. The merchants had evidently lost interest, and Raleigh's energies were being diverted elsewhere.

The accounting for a privateering voyage to the West Indies in the following year, 1591, shows Raleigh (now Watt's partner) concerned solely with high profits. He wrangled with the Queen about the prize-money which, nevertheless, brought the partnership a gross return of some £40,000, giving a profit of over 200 per cent. We find him complaining to Burghley that it was 'a small

return. We might have gotten more to have
sent them a-fishing.' When so much money was
to be made from privateering, it is small wonder
that investors were chary about speculating in
colonies which might take years to return a
modest dividend.

Raleigh claimed to have spent some £40,000
of his fortune in the struggle with Spain—a
great amount at that time for any individual to
invest. Such a sum would probably cover the
whole expediture on American voyages
between 1584 and 1588, but not all of this was
his own money, and it was not all lost, for
profits were made out of privateering in 1585
and 1586. The struggle to finance the voyages
indicates, however, the lack of any steady stream
of money available for colonies and the limits
beyond which no private person, however enthusiastic, would go in pursuit of colonial
aims.

How are we to assess Raleigh's own contribution to the American experiments? No one of
his own generation was prepared to do as much
as he to establish English settlements across the
Atlantic, but he was far from single-minded in
the efforts he made to promote colonies in the
new dominion of Virginia. His keen intellectual
interest in America and in the problems concerned with colonization is undoubted. His
hatred of Spanish power and his desire to play
a part in the overthrow of Spanish monopoly of

the overseas world was passionately sincere. Yet these objectives were qualified by his personal ambitions. If, under his auspices, successful colonies had been established, he would have achieved prestige and power as the ruler, under the Crown, of great territories, over which, if the terms of his patent were adhered to, his descendants too would rule. As the successful founder of colonies, also, he could expect to gain that pre-eminence in the councils of the country which, in spite of his closeness to Elizabeth, he never achieved.

The strength and weakness of his position was his belief that colonization must pay its way. The picture of Raleigh as an idealist, pouring out his money in pursuit of a dream of empire for the good of his country and of future generations, is, of course, quite false. He was an acute and hard-dealing business man. Colonization was a business which he undertook to promote.

That his successive expedients failed was due partly to accident and to the over-riding claims of the war with Spain, and partly to the fact that the impetus behind the colonizing movement was still a weak one, unable to mobilize the continuing expenditure of capital and effort necessary for success. Raleigh, himself, never sank more than a moderate proportion of his resources in the enterprise. It was one of many speculations in which he was engaged contemporaneously and for which he had rather a special affection, but he was never willing to gamble too much or for too long in attempting to bring it to a successful issue.

Chapter Five

An Irish Plantation

SOME months before Ralph Lane and the members of the first Virginia colony arrived in England in July 1586 after their year's sojourn in America, Sir Walter Raleigh had embarked on a new colonizing enterprise nearer home. It has already been pointed out that, from the middle of the sixteenth century, the main field for English overseas land settlement was not America but Ireland. The failure of the many projects for private and corporate colonies of English settlers in the early 'seventies had led to a temporary slump in English interest in Irish colonization, and this may have contributed to the new enthusiasm, which Gilbert and the Hakluyts did their best to stimulate, for American projects which had made possible Raleigh's experiments in Virginia.

The Munster rebellion was not at an end when Raleigh left Ireland late in 1581. From July 1579 down to the capture and execution of the sixteenth Earl of Desmond in November 1583, the whole of the southern part of the island had been seared by a long war of attrition. Although fighting had not been continuous in

129

all areas, enormous damage had been done. Castles, ecclesiastical buildings, towns and dwelling-houses had been destroyed. Much of the population of Munster had vanished, many killed without ceremony as rebels, more dying in the famine and pestilence which followed the war. Others had fled to safer parts of Ireland. The port districts alone had escaped devastation. Agriculture had disappeared from large areas, and the cattle, the chief wealth of all Irish communities, had gone with the people. Heath, bramble and furze covered the land. The only living creatures were wolves, foxes and birds. Munster was a very wilderness, which demanded some resettlement if it was to be of any future value to the English state.

With the ending of the rebellion, the Crown had acquired a vast interest in this Munster land. The attainder of Desmond, with many of his Irish and Anglo-Irish supporters, had left most of Cork, Kerry and Limerick in the hands of the Crown, together with parts of south Tipperary and western Waterford. From the beginning of 1584 there was intensive discussion in government quarters as to what should be done. Many English soldiers and officials, like Ralph Lane in Kerry, were beginning to carve out estates on paper for themselves and their friends. It was not, however, until the end of 1585 that the government made up its mind. The official scheme was the work of Burghley and Walsingham, and drew on earlier Irish plantation schemes as well as Gilbert's and Raleigh's for America. It is not unlikely that they consulted Raleigh.

The plan differed from most earlier projects in relying on state organization and direction. The Crown title to the land was confirmed by Act of Parliament in 1585. There was already a military force and civil administration in existence in Munster, and a social nucleus in the towns and in those districts which had escaped devastation. This was quite different from America. There society and administration had to start from the beginning, and consequently the risks to be run and the expenses to be borne by the state would be immeasurably greater than in Ireland. What Elizabeth's government desired in Munster was a plantation which would produce a stable, settler society, strong enough to protect itself from renewed Irish risings and prosperous enough to contribute appreciably to taxation.

The proposals agreed at the end of 1585 were for entrusting large blocks of land to a few powerful 'undertakers,' who would enlist under them enterprising groups of gentlemen as well as solid freeholders and tenant farmers, craftsmen, shopkeepers, servants and labourers, so as to transplant a whole cross-section of English society into Ireland. The large land-units, 'seignories' as they were called, were to

131

range from 4,000 to 12,000 acres of arable land,
with mountain, bog and waste land thrown in.
For each grade of seignory the undertakers were
to bring over specified numbers of gentlemen,
farmers and labourers, and were to enter into
elaborate undertakings with the government
regarding the exploitation of the land and the
exclusion of Irish from tenancies. They would
get a few rent-free years and thereafter pay rent,
low, but sufficient to contribute considerably to
revenue. In return they would get legal security
to develop the lands, and military protection
against molestation by the former owners or
wandering bands of marauders. In its working-
out, however, the plantation exhibited very
clearly the inefficiency of sixteenth-century administration, and there were repeated hitches in
bringing the scheme effectively into operation.

The government engaged in active propaganda for the settlement in the early months of
1586. Estimates were made of precisely what
investment would need to be made by each
class of settlers ranging from something under
£300 for a gentleman undertaker to less than
£6 by a cottager. A special appeal was made to
the younger sons of the gentry—a group
prominent in all schemes for improving the lot
of the middle-classes. Circulars were sent out
to justices of the peace, and several prominent
officials were sent on tours to act as travelling
salesmen for the project. Prominent courtiers

were invited to become undertakers. All this activity by the state contrasts sharply with the lack of official support for the American schemes, which, it must be appreciated, were going on contemporaneously. America was still considered a distant and risky field for private speculation, but Munster colonization was a matter of state, on which the future security of an important dominion of the Crown might depend. If Munster were left almost bare or allowed to fill up again with Irish people, then Spain might find too easy a back-door into England.

Sir Walter Raleigh was actively interested in the scheme from the beginning. During his term of service in Ireland he had tried, unsuccessfully, to get his hands on the estate of Lord Barry, comprising the Great Island in Cork Harbour and the adjoining mainland. His cousin, Sir Richard Grenville, had been interested in Irish land since the 'sixties, when he had had the nucleus of a colony in County Cork swept away by an earlier rising. In spite of the preoccupation of both men in the Virginia enterprise, they were determined to adventure in Munster on a large scale. Their previous service in Ireland and Raleigh's position at Court were in their favour in obtaining good sites in the allocation of seignories, while their extensive influence and contacts in the south-western counties helped them to get together their quotas of settlers.

There were plenty of potential speculators as

the government hawked around its scheme, though by no means all of them were serious. All through the spring, groups of gentlemen were haggling about what land they would get and on what terms. In deference to protests, the government slightly modified its original scheme in favour of the undertakers, and in June a rough attempt was made to plot out the principal seignories on the very inadequate maps which were available. It was anticipated that the settlers from particular areas of England would wish to settle together under prominent local gentlemen. In letters patent, issued on June 27, 1586, Sir Walter Raleigh was named at the head of the undertakers of Devonshire, Somerset and Dorset, along with Sir John Clifton and Sir John Stowell. Their settlement was to be in Counties Cork and Waterford and was to be organized on terms agreed with the government. Sir Richard Grenville did not immediately join in the project, but entered later with Sir Warham Saint-leger, his old partner in his earlier venture, as an undertaker for lands on the western shore of Cork Harbour.

However devastated Munster might be, it was not virgin territory. Not all the land had been legally confiscated and land-titles were chaotically tangled. A number of Irish and Anglo-Irish landholders had escaped attainder, and many were to drift back in the next few years from other parts of Ireland, claiming title to lands after they had been assigned to, and in some cases occupied by, English settlers. There was also land belonging to the towns and to the Church not available, the extent of which had to be determined. It was therefore essential that the government should know to whom it was to give what. A rough and imperfect survey of Munster had been made in 1584, and on this the first estimates were based; but it turned out to be wildly inaccurate and incomplete. On the other hand, once undertakers had received grants from the Crown in June 1586, it is not surprising that a number of them should have attempted to take possession of their lands at once. Many of them crossed with families of settlers to find that there was no one on the spot who could assign their portions at all precisely, and no arrangements had been made for their reception. After hanging about in the port towns with their retainers and colonists, most of these undertakers drifted back to England, cursing the government and determined to have nothing more to do with Irish plantations. Amongst these were Raleigh's two principal associates, Sir John Stowell and Sir John Clifton, who arrived early in the summer and returned in August. We do not know precisely what Raleigh's part was in this false start, but it is probable that he was reasonably well informed of the situation in Munster and did not send over anyone, apart from agents, to take possession of his land for him.

It was not until September that the government set commissioners to work to a make fresh survey and to assign lands to individual undertakers, and it is perhaps significant that Raleigh's lands were among the first that they started to survey. Early in October they wrote that they had spent eight days 'meting and bounding' his lands in the vicinity of Lismore and Youghal. What with the desolate and overgrown condition of the land and foul autumn weather, they found it tough going, and after a fortnight's hard work gave up until the following spring, since in any event there were no undertakers and few agents to whom the estates could be delivered.

Raleigh was not idle meanwhile. The advantage he had gained by having the lands in Cork and Waterford surveyed before the end of 1586 meant that he could make a clear start as early as he liked in the following year. On February 27, 1587, he got a Privy Seal warrant giving him a provisional title to no less than 42,000 acres of cultivable land, apart from waste land. This was a very special concession, since it had been laid down in 1586 that no undertaker was to receive more than one seignory of 12,000 acres. The grant was an indication of the Queen's special favour and expectation that he would take his new responsibilities seriously.

The River Blackwater flows from west to east through County Cork in a broadening valley and

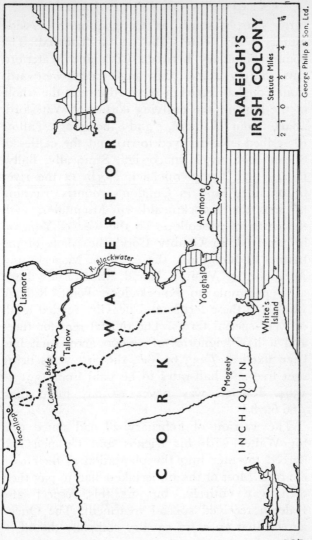

RALEIGH'S
IRISH COLONY

Statute Miles
6   4   2   1   0

George Philip & Son, Ltd.

WATERFORD

CORK

INCHIQUIN

Lismore

R. Blackwater

Tallow

Conna Bride R.

Mocollop

Mogeely

Youghal

Ardmore

White's Island

turns sharply south at Cappoquin in a wide estuary which enters the sea at Youghal. The county boundary between Cork and Waterford cuts sharply across this angle north-westwards from Youghal. Raleigh received almost the whole of the land in the outlying corner of Waterford, apart from Limore, and including Tallow (described as a decayed town) and the castles of Shean, Lisfinny, Kilnacowiga, Strancally, Ballynatray and Templemichael. North of the river he obtained land in Condon's country, running up into the Knockmealdown Mountains, with the castle of Mocollop. To the west of Youghal he received, in County Cork, the whole of the barony of Inchiquin, the castle of Mogeely and Aghavine, or White's Island, which runs down as a peninsula to Knockadoon Point. Raleigh was given these fertile and heavily wooded lands on very special terms. The official rent for three and a half seignories of 12,000 acres each had been fixed at £233 6s. 8d., the first years being rent free and half-rates to be paid from 1591 to 1594. Raleigh was never to pay more than £66 6s. 8d.

The warrant of February 28 had stated that Sir Walter with his friends and kinsmen had agreed to enter into the plantation at their own charges. Most of the undertakers had to pay their own way entirely, but in this respect also Raleigh received special treatment. The Queen agreed that an extra cavalry company should be raised to protect the intending settlers. A few of the undertakers who had special interest at Court were to supply the men from amongst the planters whom they were sending over. In fact, the scheme amounted to an indirect subsidy. Raleigh supplied the captain, Andrew Colthurst, and nineteen men, and a muster-roll of May 11 shows that they were already in Ireland and receiving the Queen's wages for doing Raleigh's work. Colthurst was, in fact, Raleigh's principal agent. He settled at Lisfinny Castle, and acted as attorney for the estate.

No elaborate expedition was needed to bring settlers to Ireland, and we do not know any details of how Raleigh collected his colonists and organized their transport. White's colonists for Virginia were also being mobilized that spring, and possibly there was a certain amount of co-operation in the organization of the two ventures. Ireland, of course, had the great advantage that small or large parties could slip across whenever they were ready and shipping was available. Certainly, throughout 1587 and 1588, men, women and children were moving into Raleigh's Irish estates.

The position of the other undertakers was not nearly so favourable. The commissioners for the survey had not taken up their work again with any speed, and consequently there were few officials who had any idea of where to place the undertakers or their agents and settlers as

139

they arrived in 1587. What happened was that those who came over grabbed what lands they could get, irrespective of title. The result was endless lawsuits with Irish and Anglo-Irish claimants. The pardon of a few native land-owners who had been attainted caused a great uproar from the undertakers and the return to the province of a number of refugees from other parts of Ireland, whose rights in the land had not necessarily been abolished with the attainder of the principal landowners, compli-cated the matter still further. The government was slow to act decisively. In 1588, however, a commission heard over eighty unsatisfied claims to land from former occupants, but dismissed all save one in favour of undertakers who had taken possession. It was two years before some kind of order was obtained out of chaos and the new land-map of the province roughed out.

Formal title was granted to Sir Walter Raleigh by an Irish patent of October 16, 1587, but it was not until the spring of 1589 that all the properties were handed over. In the mean-time he was rounding off his possessions by acquiring monastic lands from the Crown and leasing other property from private owners. Thus he gained possession of Molana Abbey, north of Youghal, the Franciscan Observant and the Dominican houses at Youghal, as well as the patronage of the wardenship of the College of

140

Our Lady, and four messuages in the town. He acquired the remainder of a lease to the castle and manor of Lismore, which belonged to the bishop, and later, in 1591, he leased from the same proprietor the manor of Ardmore, which lay opposite Youghal on the eastern side of the river estuary.

Raleigh's agents were busy in 1588 and 1589 letting property to settlers as they came over. One document lists twenty agreements for freeholds or leaseholds made in these years. The existing castles, though many were ruinous, became the homes of the new proprietors, who took responsibility, under Raleigh and his agents, for the establishment of cottagers, craftsmen and labourers. In 1589 the government, concerned over muddle and delays, appointed commissioners to investigate the situation and to get reports from the undertakers on how far they had fulfilled their contracts to bring over settlers. Raleigh's report, made on May 12, 1589, lists 144 men already settled on his estates, of whom at least seventy-three had their families with them, making a community of 300 to 400 persons already established. The great majority had been newly brought from Devonshire, Somerset and Dorset. A few were Englishmen who had been serving in Ireland, and there was also a small number of Anglo-Irish and Irish tenants. They had already a substantial number of ploughs and a stock of cattle, and were beginning to settle down to farming and the construction of village and rural life. Among the men were essential craftsmen—a miller, a smith and a baker. Gentlemen and merchants were included among the fourteen persons to whom freeholds had already been granted, and a number of farmers had leaseholds and copyholds. Raleigh was already nearly half-way to the fulfilment of his contract to place approximately 320 families on his seignories.

If any proof were needed of the closeness of the connexions between Irish and American colonizing enterprises, it is to be found in the names of the Munster settlers. Thomas Hariot was established with his family in Molana Abbey. He had published his *Briefe and True Report* in London in 1588 and had, evidently, then come over to accept the lease of the abbey lands from Raleigh. He retained his holding until about 1597, though he did not reside there continuously. He then sold his interest to William Floyer for £200. The M. Butler who was residing with his family on the Conna Bride River in 1589 was almost certainly the Michael Butler who had been Raleigh's lieutenant in Ireland in 1580–1 and who had commanded the *Bark Raleigh* when she had sailed with Gilbert in 1583. John White came later to settle in Munster, after the collapse of his last effort to find the Virginia colonists in 1590. He wrote to Richard Hakluyt early in 1593 from Newtown in Kylmore, where he had established himself. John and Robert Mawle, who became Raleigh's tenants, had subscribed to Gilbert's expedition in 1583, while John Achelley, or Ashley, was a member of a merchant family in London which had been associated with Sir George Peckham and was keenly interested in overseas enterprise. In comparing the Munster list of 1589 with the roll of Lane's colonists of 1585–6, several names are common to both though they cannot be certainly identified—James Mason, Thomas Hacket (or Hesket) and Thomas Allen, esquire ('Master Alleyne'). It would not be surprising to find Lane's men, however discouraged they were after their American adventures, coming to settle under much more advantageous terms, where their pioneering experience would still be of assistance to them.

Within two years Raleigh's plantation had achieved what had been planned for White's Virginia colonists of 1587, a settlement containing in itself the elements of self-sufficiency and the seeds of future growth. Munster, if it had not the vines and tobacco of Virginia, had in the short-run many advantages. Chief among them was easy access by sea to England and a chain of established ports—Waterford, Dungarvan, Youghal, Cork and Kinsale—which, though small, had markets and facilities for export and import. Such assets could well be decisive. No stage of American colonization proved so difficult as the construction of the first bases of white settlement.

Raleigh's colony was not the only one making headway in Munster, though the most outstanding. On twenty-three other seignories some 500 male settlers were returned in 1589 as resident, making perhaps about 1,000 persons in all. Apart from Raleigh, the most successful undertakers were Sir Warham Saintleger and Sir Richard Grenville. Grenville, like Raleigh, had evidently learned much from American mistakes. Other undertakers were much less effective. Many could show only a few settlers and several none at all. The Irish inhabitants were drifting back and were being taken as labourers by the farmers in all the seignories. Some who refused to accept the seizure of their former property took to the woods and bogs and lived the life of bandits and outcasts, but a number of the undertakers, rather than go to the worry and expense of bring over English tenants, were letting land to the Irish, contrary to the plantation agreements, so that many natives came back to their old lands as tenants of an English proprietor who was often an absentee. Thus the more modern type of English exploitation of Irish lands was already taking shape. In time, over most of the island, it was to swamp the attempt to make all the farmers Englishmen and all towns English, while the Irish would be left only servile tasks. In fact, the main wealth from the lands taken by the English from the Irish and Anglo-Irish in the sixteenth and seventeenth centuries was to come from rents paid by Irish tenant-farmers.

Even though Raleigh had performed the first part of his bargain with the Crown successfully his quota of 320 families involved bringing altogether about 1,000 persons. Unfortunately, there is little direct evidence of how the plantation developed during the following years. A new investigation of its progress was made in 1592, but the commissioners did not bother to obtain the details of the settlement on Raleigh's lands, and the only item of information which they gave was that he had begun to pay rent at half-rates to the Crown.

It was not until the autumn of 1588 that Raleigh visited the extensive lands he had acquired in Munster. In September he and Sir Richard Grenville convoyed some reinforcements for the English garrison to Ireland, and both then passed on to inspect their Irish properties. Raleigh stayed for three months in Munster, where his agents, Colthurst and Robert Mawle, appear to have been reasonably efficient and not too entirely absorbed in feathering their own nests. But there was much legal work for him to do, while he had to discover how his estate could be developed most profitably. He was also concerned to establish households for himself at Youghal and Lismore. He took a fancy to the fifteenth-century house of the warden of the college in Youghal and had it made into a pleasant residence. Hayman,[1] the historian of Youghal, says that he also accepted the mayoralty of the town for the year 1588–9. At Lismore, too, he began putting the castle into shape for his own use.

In 1589 he was in Munster again, possibly by July and certainly in August. His cousin, Sir George Carew, recently appointed master of the ordnance in Ireland, visited Raleigh at Lismore on September 26. After his return to England he asked Carew to finance the building works he had put in hand at Lismore until money could be transferred from England for the purpose. Raleigh also saw something of Edmund Spenser, whom he had probably known as Lord Grey's secretary and who now held the neighbouring seignory of Kilcolman farther up the Blackwater. Spenser accompanied him to England in October, and apparently found the introductions Raleigh gave him of some value at Court. Their friendship is of some importance for English literature, since, through it, the first three books of the *Faerie Queene* found, in 1590, an earlier publication than they otherwise might, while Spenser's verse reflects the mutual liking and respect of the two poets and colonizers.

While in Ireland Raleigh was more pre-

[1] S. Hayman, *Notes of the Ancient Religious Foundations at Youghal* (1855), pp. 58–9.

occupied with lawsuits than with poetry. He soon fell foul of the crusty old Lord Deputy, Sir William Fitzwilliam, and during the whole period of his deputyship, from 1588 to 1594, there was friction between them. This antagonism caused Raleigh a good deal of trouble, some of which he brought on himself by his own arrogance. Towards the end of 1586 or early in 1587, Raleigh had acquired a lease of Lismore from one Parker, who said he had a title to it from the Bishop of Waterford and Lismore. There was, however, in existence another lease in the hands of Sir William Stanley, who had held important military commands in Ireland and had been mentioned as the leader of one of Sir George Peckham's projected expeditions to America in 1582. Stanley had sub-let to John Egerton and two other men, and he had gone to the Netherlands with some Irish troops to assist Leicester. There he suddenly deserted to the Spaniards at Deventer in 1587. In the meantime, his wife had appealed to the Privy Council in England for the return of Lismore to Egerton. The council was sympathetic and referred the case to the Lord Deputy, Sir John Perrot. No decision had been reached when Fitzwilliam became deputy, and Raleigh failed to get one in his favour on either of his visits to Ireland, though after his return in 1589 Fitzwilliam began to take action detrimental to his claims.

Fitzwilliam, Raleigh thought, had heard a

rumour that he had fallen from favour at Court and on December 27, 1589, he wrote a scathing letter to Carew. 'When Sir William Fitzwilliam shall be in England,' he said, 'I take myself far his better by the honourable offices I hold, as also by that nearness to her majesty which still I enjoy and never more. If in Ireland they think I am not worth the respecting, they shall much deceive themselves. I am in place to be believed not inferior to any man, to pleasure or displeasure the greatest; and my opinion is so received and believed as I can anger the best of them.' The main quarrel was about Lismore. 'For the suit of Lismore,' Raleigh said, 'I will shortly send over order from the Queen for a dismiss of their "cavelacions." ' In no letter of his is Raleigh's arrogance better illustrated or his willingness to twist the law in his own favour. He was right about Lismore. On April 10, 1590, the Queen wrote to Fitzwilliam about Lady Stanley's suit, 'for as much as we consider how inconvenient it that the said traitor's wife, or any of his favourers, should in any way receive countenance, we command you that ye presently take order for staying any such suit already commenced or hereafter to be commenced by her or any other person for her, either for lands or for any other matter between our servant and her, until we signify our further pleasure in this behalf.' Needless to say, nothing more was heard of the suit, and Raleigh retained Lismore. Thus could the law be adapted to the needs of a powerful courtier.

A much larger matter had arisen before Raleigh's second visit to Ireland. A draft letter from the Queen to Fitzwilliam in June 1589 had stated that Raleigh should surrender his great domain of 42,000 acres and receive instead a single seignory of 12,000, thus being brought into line with the other undertakers. The letter was never sent and Raleigh retained possession of his whole grant, but this issue probably underlay the continuing bitterness between Raleigh and Fitzwilliam. In June 1590, for example, Fitzwilliam made an order to protect William Hetherington's possession of lands at Kilbeg, County Waterford, against Raleigh's agent, Robert Mawle. Then, too, when Raleigh really was in disgrace in 1592 Fitzwilliam increased his pressure. In a letter to Sir Robert Cecil towards the end of 1592, Raleigh made a long series of complaints. Fitzwilliam had, he said, demanded the sum of £400 alleged to be due in rent to the Crown. He had sent the sheriff to distrain on Raleigh's tenants, who had seized 500 milch cows from the settlers. 'Some had but two and some three to relieve their poor wives and children, and in a strange country newly set down to build and plant,' Raleigh remarked. Raleigh said that the sum involved was in reality £33 6s. 8d., and that it had been paid. In both these assertions he was right and Fitzwilliam wrong. The deputy had also, he declared, forced his agents to relinquish a castle which had been rebuilt and planted with English settlers, while the soldiers from Youghal were spoiling the country and driving away his best tenants. 'It will,' he concluded, 'be no small weakening to the Queen in those parts, and no small comfort to the ill-affected Irish, to have the English inhabitants driven out of the country.' In another letter a little later, and also to Cecil, he said, 'your cousin, the doting deputy, hath dis-peopled me. It is a sign how my disgraces have passed the seas and have been highly com-mended to that wise governor, who hath used me accordingly. So I leave to trouble you at this time, being become like a fish cast on dry land, gasping for breath, with lame legs and lamer lungs.' In less than three years his arrogance had been turned against him: in 1590 he could trample on Fitzwilliam, in 1592 he must submit to be trampled.

In fairness to Fitzwilliam, it may be said that though he had wronged Raleigh in distraining for a debt not due, he had a deep-seated distrust of decorative courtiers who could pull strings with the Queen and a hatred of the sycophancy he needed to keep himself in office. His bitter marginal comments on the letters he received from English suitors and his earnest desire to get on with his own job show him to have been a man of principle. It is small wonder that he was infuriated by Raleigh's high-handed action over the Stanley estate. The controversy illustrates something more than personal differences. In America, had Raleigh established a colony there, he would have been sovereign, subject only to the Crown. In Ireland he had, within limits, to submit to the established laws and officials. Ireland's advantage for settlers, in possessing some existing fabric of administration, has been emphasized. But there was less freedom there than in America, whether for dissident groups in the English community or for speculators like Raleigh, who wished for power as well as wealth from their overseas lands. The divergent attractions of Ireland and America continued for most of the seventeenth century, but ultimately the American magnet proved the more powerful.

Not all the new settlers settled down at once and prospered. Some were unsuitable and either drifted home or into poverty. Almost all had a hard task to build dwellings, clear and cultivate land and find a market for their produce. The terms were stiff enough. One lease from Raleigh to John Clever, gentleman of London dated July 21, 1588, of 400 acres of arable land in the barony of Inchiquin, gives some idea of the conditions binding the tenants. Clever was to pay, after 1593, £10 sterling a year on a 100 years' lease, with eight capons. He had to provide on call an armed horse-soldier for service in the province. He was to build 'one mansion or dwelling house' and 'enclose with hedge, ditch and quickset, one hundred acres, and keep the same in good and sufficient reparation and fencing.' Waste or barren ground reclaimed was to be paid for at 1*d.* an acre, if the Crown should make any further demand on Raleigh's estate. The tenant 'also shall leave at every fall of any of the woods of the same premises twenty and five stands in every acre, according to the custom of England.' Farmers of ability, who happened to get good land accessible to a town or navigable river, probably did well enough, but many preferred to live on rents from Irish tenants and to engage in land-jobbing and commercial speculation.

In 1588 a writer suggested to Burghley that most of the glass manufactories in England should be removed to Munster as 'the woods in England will be thereby preserved and the superfluous woods wasted, than which in tyme of rebellion her majesty hath no greater enemy there.' Timber, indeed, was a headache for enterprising English manufacturers. The growth of the iron and shipbuilding industries was increasing home timber-consumption and causing alarm by heavy wastage. Overseas timber supplies were coveted, though, apart from the rarer woods, transport across the Atlantic, for example, was not an economic proposition. The most immediately exploitable natural wealth in Munster was its timber, and Raleigh's lands were especially well-wooded. While it is probable that within a few years the estate was showing a net profit from the leases made to the settler-tenants, he determined to try to exploit the timber as well. In 1589, in partnership with two Englishmen, Henry Pyne and Edward Dodge, and a Dutchman, Veronio Martens, he got a royal licence to export from Munster all commodities whether or not there were legal restrictions on their export. With Pyne as his agent, Raleigh immediately initiated a large-scale trade in the timber of the Blackwater woods. This was, for the most part, made into pipe-staves and hogshead-staves for the wine-producing Atlantic islands, the Canaries and Madeira, with which England continued to trade for wine and sugar throughout the war with Spain. Some of the heavier timber was cut into planks for English warships. In less than three years Raleigh claimed that some 340,000 staves had been exported in twelve ships, a capital investment of £5,000 had been made in saw-mills and other equipment, and some 200 workers, mostly English settlers, had been set to work. The centre of the industry was Mogeely, where Pyne was the tenant of the castle, and the sawn timber was carried on horse-back to the river for transport to Youghal and thence overseas.

Just when the business was getting into its

stride, in 1592, it was suddenly brought to a standstill by an order from Fitzwilliam forbidding all further exports, while Pyne was arrested and brought to Dublin. The charges were that barrel-staves were being exported to Spain as well as to the Atlantic islands, and that heavy planking, suitable for shipbuilding, was going as well. Pyne was further charged with acting as a channel of information between Catholic refugees on the continent and recusants in Ireland and England. These were serious charges. Fitzwilliam also expressed alarm at the denudation of the woodlands and at the support Pyne and Raleigh were giving to Patrick Condon, an Irish landowner, who had been belatedly pardoned and who was trying to recover his former lands north of the Blackwater from another undertaker, Arthur Hyde.

Consequently, Raleigh was involved in rather a nasty scandal, and he did his best, in spite of his disgrace, to mobilize his friends in the Privy Council to throw out the charges. The defence was a denial of the export of anything but barrel-staves to the Atlantic islands, a claim that only small quantities of timber were being used, and a repudiation of the charges of intelligence with the enemy. Pyne was interrogated in England on the treachery charge in July but cleared himself, and at the end of August was petitioning for the renewal of the export trade. This request was eventually granted and on January

21, 1594, Raleigh and his partners were permitted to resume export of staves for pipes and hogsheads to the Islands, Bordeaux and La Rochelle, but not to metropolitan Spain.

Pyne went back to Mogeely and restarted the industry rapidly and efficiently, though he caused some trouble in 1596 by claiming that the licence of 1594 gave the partnership a monopoly of timber exports. It is likely that most of the profits went into his own pockets. The government continued to be concerned about the denudation of timber resources, and an official, William Waad, was appointed by the Crown to supervise timber cutting and exports in England and Ireland. However, Pyne had Waad's authority in Ireland delegated to himself and was therefore able to carry on the business and keep other competitors out.

About 1594 Raleigh thought of another way in which the timber on his estates might be used. Iron ore had been discovered, and on July 20, 1594, he wrote to Cecil that he was then preparing fifty Cornish miners 'for which I had direction.' Possibly they were being sent to Munster to commence extraction. With timber on the spot, iron-working offered an attractive speculation. In 1595 Raleigh licensed George Goring and Herbert Pelham to erect iron-mills on his land and to use local timber for smelting. They brought over workmen, but found that Raleigh's tenants obstructed the establishment of the industry, apparently because the lands which had been assigned to them by Raleigh had been let by his agents to other tenants without his knowledge. Pyne, too, would have some incentive to oppose another industry, which might compete with his own by offering higher prices for timber. Goring and Pelham got letters of assistance from the Privy Council, but it is not certain that they succeeded in founding a smelting industry at this time. Raleigh did not lose interest in the exploitation of minerals, and in 1602 we find Carew writing to Cecil to say, 'I sent unto Sir Walter Raleigh many sorts of ore. I would be glad to know how they prove and that speedily.' Later, after Raleigh had disposed of his Munster properties, iron-smelting was established on a considerable scale and copper-mining begun.

The Irish rebellion in 1598 enabled Pyne to consolidate his own position in the timber business to the detriment of his other partners, and in 1601 they accused him of converting both capital and profits to his own use. The Privy Council ordered that exports be stopped until Pyne had come to England and answered their charges. But, eventually, Raleigh, Martens and Bathurst (who had replaced Dodge as a partner) settled their differences with Pyne.

Some detailed attention had been paid to these commercial and industrial activities as they form a significant aspect of Raleigh's attempt to develop an overseas property. A subsistence agriculture alone might keep settlers alive, but it was scarcely likely to make the promotor of the plantation rich. Timber provided a staple export, which gave employment in Munster and profit to Raleigh, and was comparable with tobacco in Jacobean Virginia. In spite of the restrictive covenants imposed on Raleigh's tenants, the destruction of the woods appears to have been largely unchecked. For Ireland this was somewhat disastrous, but for the colony it provided a means of growth and development such as the Virginia colony was to find only after much suffering and trial and error. It was further necessary for complete security either to establish permanent good relations with the natives whose land and labour were being exploited, or else suppress or extirpate them effectively. Just as the Virginia colony, at last beginning to make real progress, was almost wiped out and its development impeded for years by the Indian rising of 1622, so the Munster plantation received an almost mortal blow by the Irish rising of 1598 and the four subsequent years of warfare.

Ever since the plantation began, it had been harried in some districts by outlawed and disaffected Irishmen with a price on their heads or families who had refused to accept peacefully dispossession from their lands; while the Irish working for the settlers and providing them with undertenants had steadily increased and, though temporarily quiescent, had never been reconciled. Consequently when, from 1594, Hugh O'Neill, second Earl of Tyrone, began building up his Ulster lordship into a formidable bastion against the English power, the Irish and some of the Anglo-Irish of Munster began to consolidate the little groups of outlaws into formidable bands of resolute and desperate men. During 1598 the raids on the settlements increased. Planters worried Sir Thomas Norris, president of Munster, for protection and redress: 'Why must *I* keep thy cows?' was his reply! Not mere robbery but the threat of a new rising faced the settlers. Hugh O'Neill's prowess in repelling English attacks in Ulster affected, successively, Leinster, Connacht and Munster. Organized by O'Neill's guerrilla officers, the Munster Irish rose suddenly in October 1598. Widespread attacks were made on the planters before defence was organized. Men, women and children were either killed or driven headlong into the port towns, which alone resisted attacks and from which they might make their way to England. There was much panic, which affected Raleigh's tenants among the rest. 'All the English of the seignory of Sir Walter Raleigh, namely John Harris, William Andrew, with others, ran away,' we are told, while in Tallow, 'a great town, all the English, man and woman and child, where there were thirty good shot, and in all about

three score able men, ran away every one.'
Henry Pyne was even able to anticipate the
rising, and departed before it broke out, his
action causing some comment after the outbreak.

Youghal, Lismore and Mogeely held out
against insurgent attacks. Pyne recovered his
courage and returned to make money out of
victualling the English forces in Youghal. In
1599 he commanded the garrison stationed in
Mogeely, and the following year he was back in
London, giving a graphic account of the
attempts of the rebels to capture the castle and
of his own skill in foiling them. Pyne rode the
storm, but most of the settlers did not. From
Cork and Youghal they drifted to their home-
land, colonists who had failed.

The trail of rebellion crossed and recrossed
Munster during the years after 1598. In 1601
Kinsale drew attention from all Europe. With
a Spanish force entrenched in the port and with
Hugh O'Neill and Hugh O'Donnell riding with
their cavalry to the south, the day of the insurgent Irish appeared to have come. But all their
hopes vanished with the smashing defeat of the
Ulster and Munster Irish, followed by the
capitulation of the Spaniards. Under the able
direction of Sir George Carew, the bands
remaining in Munster were rapidly crushed. By
1602 peace was returning to the province, a
peace not dissimilar to that of 1583. But this
time it was the houses and farms of English

colonists which lay burnt and waste. Though a Munster settlement was rebuilt in parts of the former area, it was never able to have the same vitality again. Most of its English were to remain landlords, often absentees and not tillers of the soil, for three centuries until the Irish came at last to own their lands again.

Even before the Munster rising, Raleigh was apparently beginning to tire of his Munster responsibilities. Continuous lawsuits hampered and irritated him, while Pyne was busy exploiting him as well as his fellow-settlers. On May 27, 1598, Raleigh conveyed his Irish lands to his friend Thomas Southwell. The details of the transaction do not appear to have survived but, whatever its precise import, it did not involve the surrender of Raleigh's own title. The loss and destruction sustained in 1598 and the following years, with the ruin of the most promising settlements such as Tallow, completed his disillusionment. Sir George Carew in 1602 was looking out for a purchaser for him, and he found a possible one in the shrewd, thrusting secretary of the Munster presidency, Robert Boyle. He sent Boyle over to see Raleigh, and they came to an agreement on December 7, 1602, by which Boyle got the whole property for £1,500. The smallness of the purchase money has led to some speculation, but is explained by Carew's statement that by 1602 the Munster seignories, instead of yielding any profit, were costing Raleigh some £200 a year. To revive the profitability of the lands new capital, new settlers and new energy were required, and Raleigh had no more to spare for Ireland. Boyle had plenty of energy and ability, but little money. He paid down £500 in cash, but the rest was outstanding when Raleigh was attainted in 1603. James I tried to upset the uncompleted bargain and get his hands on the property which would otherwise have reverted to the Crown, but Boyle finally got his title confirmed by paying over the outstanding £1,000 to the King in 1604.

Raleigh visited Lismore once again, on his way to Guiana in 1617. He stayed with Boyle, now a great magnate with a flourishing estate far larger than Raleigh had ever owned, and, borrowing some money which Boyle could not well refuse, set out on his fatal last voyage. He saw Ireland again in May 1618, when the *Destiny* put into Kinsale for a few days on his way to England and his death.

Chapter Six

The Beautiful Empire

SIR WALTER RALEIGH had never confined his interest in the colonial world to North America. It was for the West Indies he had set course in 1578, and he had settled down to read the history of the Spanish empire and to accumulate knowledge of it from Spanish prisoners, from French sailors and from English privateers and traders. In 1596 he tells us himself that he had written 'a particular treatise of the West Indies,' which has not survived. For efficient privateering it was necessary for him to know the workings of the Spanish colonial system and to work out vulnerable points; but his interest went far beyond that. He became convinced that England could and must destroy Spanish power by the disruption of her American empire.

The commonly accepted theory was that if the commerce and treasure of the New World were intercepted at sea, then the Spanish empire would gradually be wasted away. Yet, though Spain lost much at sea and England gained vitally important capital, both for her defence and her subsequent industrial development, this was not a practical solution. England was too weak at sea to close the routes between America and Spain. Drake and many others had from the early 'seventies held that the seizure of the Panama Isthmus would provide a means of stopping the flow of bullion from Peru, and he and Hawkins were to make a last unsuccessful attempt to do this in 1595-6; but as Raleigh said, 'the king of Spain is not so impoverished by taking three or four port towns in America as we suppose, neither are the riches of Peru or Nueva España so left by the seaside, as it can be easily washed away, with a great flood, or spring tide, or left dry upon the sand in a low ebb.'

These solutions were both negative and partial. Raleigh sought finality. 'It is his Indian gold,' he said, 'that endangereth and disturbeth all the nations of Europe, it purchaseth intelligence, creepeth into councils, and setteth bound loyalty at liberty, in the greatest monarchies of Europe.' A solution was, therefore, to find comparable sources of bullion which would be wholly at England's disposal, so that Spain might be prised out of her pre-eminence. Somehow a comparably rich overseas empire must be created.

Raleigh's interest finally focused on Guiana, the name then given to the northern part of the Amazon and the whole of the Orinoco basins. He had collected and collated many accounts by the Spanish explorers who had pushed eastwards from the Andes in the past half-century. It was probably in 1584 that his attention was first drawn to the possibilities of the zone between the Amazon and the Orinoco as offering a possible means of entry into a part of the mainland of South America not yet effectively occupied by the Spaniards or Portuguese.

Richard Hakluyt may have had a good deal to do with developing his interest. In the *Discourse of Western Planting* he had spent some time in explaining that the hold of the Spaniards was by no means effective over the whole of the vast territories which they claimed, and, in particular, drew attention to the absence of posts in the region east of Cumana. He said:

> 'All that part of America eastward from Cumana unto the river of St. Augustine in Brazil containeth in length along the sea side 2,100 miles. In which compass and tract there is neither Spaniard, Portingale nor any Christian man but only the Caribs, Indians and savages. In which places is great plenty of gold, pearl and precious stones.'

In the same year, at Falmouth, Raleigh spoke to a French captain who had been on the Amazon. Already English and French merchants and privateers were taking advantage of the absence of Spanish and Portuguese settlements to build up something of a trade with the native inhabitants of this region. Both French and

English had long been interested in the more southerly parts of Brazil, and had traded with both natives and Portuguese settlers, while the French had tried to establish a colony there. During the ten years from 1584, however, French and, especially, English privateers and traders had paid special attention to Trinidad. They found it easy to get food from the Indians. Even before 1595 some English ships had gone specially to collect tobacco, and some Indians had been brought to England and taken back as intermediaries with the native rulers. Raleigh had one of these native interpreters with him at Trinidad. The approach to Guiana was therefore well known and the Trinidad natives formed one source of information on the wonders of El Dorado.

In 1586 Raleigh learnt more about South America from a Spanish expert. Captain Jacob Whiddon, with the *Serpent* and *Mary Spark*, had gone out in June to pick up prizes for Raleigh. Amongst the prisoners brought back was the Spanish official, Don Pedro Sarmiento de Gamboa. He had been with Mendaña at the discovery of the Solomons in 1567–8, and had given chase to Drake in the Pacific in 1579. Subsequently, his task had been to found a colony on the Strait of Magellan in 1581. Three years later he had gone off to seek reinforcements in Brazil, and was now on his way to Spain on a similar mission while his colony was dying.

Raleigh met him on his arrival and found they had much in common, and it is probable that they discussed the relative problems of founding colonies in Patagonia and in North Carolina. Sarmiento knew much of the conquest of Peru and of attempts to find El Dorado somewhere in the vast area to the east of the Andes. He had himself written on this subject, and it is almost certainly he of whom Raleigh said in 1596: 'Many years since, I had knowledge by relation, of that mighty, rich and beautiful Empire of Guiana, and of that great and golden city, which the Spaniards call El Dorado and the naturals Manoa.' Sarmiento saw the Queen and Burghley as well as Raleigh, and was sent home without any ransom being asked. Apparently he offered to attempt to discuss with Philip the possibility of restoring peaceful trade relations between England and Spain. Certainly he gave Raleigh assurances of friendship, and may also have promised to send him information on El Dorado. For his part, Raleigh indicated that he was friendly towards the King of Spain and wished to avoid open war between the two countries. Both were playing a deceitful game so far as national issues were concerned, but Raleigh's offer to sell ships to Spain was not one to deceive for long.

There was nothing static about the Spanish empire in the latter half of the sixteenth century. An elaborate system of administrative control had not yet cramped initiative, and there was a constant search for new areas and new products to be exploited within the wide territories of the American empire. The search for a second Inca civilization, rich in gold and located to the east of the Andes, had gone on from 1530. It had been sought up the Amazon and down its many tributaries, which flowed eastwards from the Andes. Many remarkable journeys had been made and many lives had been lost. Gradually, the legend had crystallized out of Indian stories and travellers' tales. Its essentials were simple. Somewhere in the interior there was a great civilized empire. Its name was El Dorado, the gilded one, so-called from the ritual of its ruler, who powdered himself over with gold-dust and ceremonially bathed in a lake which formed the centre of his dominions. Manoa, his capital, rivalled the wealth of the cities of Peru. Gradually, too, the location of this mythical empire had been narrowed down to the Guiana Highlands, a great inland plateau, which could be reached only through the thick coastal forests or from the difficult basin of the Orinoco River.

The man mainly responsible for the definition and location of El Dorado was Don Antonio de Berrio. In 1580, at the age of sixty, he had acquired a great fortune and a mission, and for fifteen years before Raleigh's arrival in Trinidad in 1595, he had made constant expeditions in

167

search of his objective. In his first expedition in 1584–5 he made his way from Tunja in New Granada eastwards down the tributaries of the Orinoco to the main stream, which he crossed towards the promising mountain range which lay to the west. He was not able to ascend into and explore the mountains, and returned to New Granada with information gleaned from the Indians that in the highlands was a civilized empire round a great lake and rich in gold and cities. He sent back news of his discoveries and speculations to Spain, urged that Trinidad be colonized and Guiana given him to govern, and was sent back a commission as governor of 'El Dorado' or Guiana.

On his second expedition, lasting from 1585 to 1588, he again approached and crossed the Orinoco from the west and probed the fringes of the mountains for a passable means of entry into the Highlands, but the plateau was ringed with a steep escarpment and he failed and again had to return. Finally, in 1590, he got together a third force, retraced his steps and explored eastwards from his previous limits down the right bank of the Orinoco and in its hinterland. He finally decided to work down-stream to the Caroni, which he learnt would give him entry through the maintains, but on reaching there he had not the men or equipment to surmount its gorge and cataract. Living off—and exploiting—the Indians, he won their hostility and finally limped down to Trinidad on September 1, 1591. Back in contact with the Spanish settlement on Margarita, he found the governor, Don Juan Sarmiento de Villandrando, suspicious, jealous and unhelpful. However, joining forces with a certain Domingo de Vera Ybarguen, he was able to get enough support from Osorio, the governor of Venezuela, to establish the small post of San Josef on Trinidad in 1592 as a base for future operations. Both Sarmiento and Osorio aspired to explore the Orinoco for Berrio's El Dorado, and a third competitor, Francisco de Vides, arrived as governor of Cumana, with authority to colonize Trinidad, at the end of 1592. De Vera went up towards the Caroni in 1593, and got from the Indians what seemed to be precise information that some 250 miles up the Caroni basin there was a lake where a great civilized population had appeared and settled some twenty years before. He got back in May, and sent a report to Spain. In fact, the Indians appear to have referred to the swollen, lake-like Paragua, a tributary of the Caroni, and to the appearance on it of an immigrant tribe of somewhat advanced people. This mixture of fact and legend seemed to provide a fairly precise location for El Dorado.

Berrio hung on at Trinidad, allocating land to his soldiers, exploiting the natives and at last getting, in 1594, a reinforcement from New Granada. He sent de Vera off to Spain for more substantial aid, which he was awaiting when Raleigh arrived in 1595, and he had stationed a few men at the village of Carapana near the Orinoco estuary. Raleigh, by one means or another, learnt the outline and some details of Berrio's achievements and theories. In 1595 he was to hear more of them from Berrio himself.

The graph of Raleigh's personal fortune had been a rapid ascent from 1581 to 1587, but in the next ten years it was subject to violent fluctuations. It was these which sent him in person on the road to Guiana in 1595. The appearace of the attractive, headstrong and violent young Earl of Essex at Court meant a serious challenge in that charmed circle of the Queen's intimates, where Raleigh had been supreme for some years. Essex's outspoken attack on Raleigh in 1587 won him royal reproof but did not exclude him from favour, and the following years saw bitter intrigues between them and their supporters at Court, each having their victories and defeats, each keeping the Queen's affection, Essex the more intimately, Raleigh the more steadily. The Queen's entourage was changing and her old officers of state dying off. Walsingham's death in 1590 was a blow to Raleigh's standing. He continued to be excluded from the Privy Council and from high state office, while the struggle for place and power round the old Queen, whose judgment grew less and less calculable, became embittered. After the defeat of the *armada* domestic politics changed fast. Parties at Court were coming to represent divergent social and economic interests in the country, and the alliance between the Crown, the gentry and the merchants was beginning to break up. The last fifteen years of the Tudor period saw the hatching of many of the controversies which were to break down the Stuart monarchy in a middle-class revolution.

The mature Raleigh of these tangled years was a complex personality, full of paradoxes and inconsistencies in thought and action. Where his own interests were concerned he pushed ruthlessly along the orthodox roads to power and influence, but he was unable to repress his keen critical intelligence and his pride, which made him sceptical and contemptuous of accepted values. Thus, though he derived much of his income from monopolies granted to him by royal favour, he could speak in Parliament in favour of freedom of trade. Though professedly orthodox in religion, he could risk the charge of atheism for his readiness to discuss sceptically problems of theology, philosophy and morals, while he was prepared to defend nonconformist Brownists from persecution. A courtier by long training, ready to fawn on a powerful minister and to crawl before the Queen, or, corruptly, to obtain a bishopric for one of his tools, he yet despised Court life and could write:

Say to the Court it glowes
And shines like rotten wood.
Say to the Church it showes
What's good and doth no good.
If Church and Court reply,
Then give them both the lie.

The same inconsistency is found in his political views. Though ostensibly a defender of monarchy and owing everything to the favour of a virtually absolute Queen, he attacked in his writings the tyranny of princes. He is constantly found urging the government to give national interests precedence over private ones in the conflict with Spain, while at the same time he was feathering his own nest to the best of his ability. In his own privateering ventures, his greed for profits made him justify attacks on neutral shipping which gravely embarrassed the government. His fellow-adventurers accused him of cheating them. He wrangled fiercely with the Queen over their respective shares in the spoil won from the sea.

It is not surprising that his pride and arrogance made enemies, though his generosity to those who served him and his respect for those whom he regarded as his intellectual equals won him devoted friends. But he was too intelligent to be a wholly successful courtier and too incalculable in debate and in action to make a dependable statesman. Distrusted, he was kept out of positions of crucial responsibility. Yet he knew his own powers and had great ambitions, and potentially he was, unsatisfied, a dangerous man.

Action at sea was Raleigh's response to increased competition at Court. In the autumn of the *armada* year he and Grenville convoyed troops to Ireland and stood by with their ships in case any of the defeated Spanish vessels creeping down the west coast showed fight. The following year he was an adventurer in Drake's Portugal voyage, possibly in person, but in any event sharing, to the amount of £4,000, in the spoil of Lisbon. He helped to plan the 1591 expedition designed to take the treasure-fleet at sea, and planned to go, with Lord Thomas Howard, as joint commander. When the Queen intervened, Sir Richard Grenville went in his place, in the *Revenge*, as vice-admiral of a much smaller squadron than had originally been contemplated. The vessels, three of them commanded by Raleigh's later companions in the Guiana voyage—Whiddon, Cross and Thynne —loitered off the Azores. At the end of August they were surprised by a Spanish fleet coming from the east. Grenville, in the *Revenge*, was surrounded: he fought hard until his crew gave up after he had been mortally wounded, and sank two of the attacking vessels and damaged many others. Raleigh commemorated Grenville's dying exploit in his first published prose work, *A report of the truth of the fight about the Iles of Açores, this last summer. Betwixt the Revenge, one of her Maiesties shippes, and an armada of the king of Spaine.* In it he made a bitter attack on Spain, which he accused of aggression all over Europe under the pretext of religion: 'neither have they,' he continued, 'at any time as they protest invaded the kingdoms of the Indies and Peru, and elsewhere, but only led thereunto rather, to reduce the people to Christianity, than for either gold or empire. When as in one only island called Hispaniola, they have wasted thirty hundred thousand of the natural people, besides many millions else in other places of the Indies: a poor and harmless people.' This was a propaganda line taken up in many ways by the government in its struggle with Spain, but it also provided one pretext— the rescue of the natives from Spanish tyranny— for intervention in Guiana.

To pay off scores for the loss of the *Revenge*, Raleigh helped to plan an attack on the Isthmus of Panama, which he was to lead. The Queen adventured two ships and £3,000, while Raleigh contributed the *Roebuck* and much of his own and borrowed money. But again the Queen would not let him go, and he agreed that he would only accompany the fleet to the coast of Spain. It did not sail until May 6, and then it was too late to hope to catch the Spanish treasure fleet before it left America. Consequently, the attempt to capture it at sea was renewed. On

May 7 Frobisher caught up with Raleigh with peremptory orders from the Queen to return. He ignored them, and with Sir John Burgh, the new commander, made his dispositions at sea. Frobisher was assigned to watch the Spanish coast, while the rest of the squadron went on to the Azores. Only then did Raleigh turn homewards. Burgh joined with some of the Earl of Cumberland's privateers, and encountered, not American fleet, but two great carracks coming from the Portuguese East Indies. The *Santa Cruz* was driven ashore, set on fire and provided only some pickings from her rich cargo. The *Madre de Dios*, 1,600 tons, was boarded and taken. All the way to England she was being looted by the sailors, who took her portable wealth to many widely scattered ports. Eventually, five weeks after her capture, on Septmber 8, the great prize was brought into Dartmouth.

By this time Raleigh had spent some weeks as a prisoner in the Tower. Back at Plymouth on May 18, he was not punished for his disobedience until a new example of his lack of scruple came to light. On or about February 20, 1592, Raleigh had secretly married Elizabeth Throckmorton, a maid of honour at Court. Rumours had circulated while he was still preparing to sail, but he denied them categorically to Sir Robert Cecil on March 10, saying 'I protest before God there is none on the face of the earth that I would be fastened unto', and is likely to have said the same to the Queen. He relied on success at sea to cool the Queen's anger at the desertion of one of her courtier-lovers, but he was wrong. His blatant deceit, the extent, apparently, of the Queen's attachment to him, her jealousy of his wife, and the intrigues of his enemies at Court brought disaster. In July, apparently on the 31st, he and his wife were imprisoned.[1]

Prison was a terrible blow to his pride. The check it gave to his career was also a turning-point in his life. For nearly five years Elizabeth turned away from him, her anger and displeasure cooling only slowly to re-acceptance: when at last he regained her confidence it was on a less intimate basis. For Elizabeth it was the douche of very cold water she felt he needed. In September she let him out on a string to act as one of the commissioners sent down to Dartmouth to sort out the affair of the *Madre de Dios*, for as soon as the great prize arrived in port more pillage started and bullion and precious stones were being widely dispersed. Raleigh, with Robert Cecil, Drake and other commissioners, managed to get back some of the loot and to salve the heavier cargo, including a great quantity of pepper. The Queen cleared the greater part of £82,666 13s. 4d., for which the pepper was sold,

---

[1] See P. Lefranc in *Etudes anglaises*, ix (1956), 193–211 (with a document which seems to give Feb. 20, 1588 (*recte* 1592?), for the marriage).

in payment for her investment of two ships and £3,000. Raleigh and his partners claimed to have sunk £34,000 in the venture and to have got £36,000 only. For £6,000 the London companies got double and Cumberland, for £19,000 got £36,000. Raleigh mentioned £6,000 of his own money and £11,000 he borrowed as part of his personal adventure: he got back £24,000, but from the published documents it is not clear whether in fact, as he said, he lost money by the transaction. But for his imprisonment he might, however, have become fabulously rich, and this rankled, though he said magniloquently he was glad to give the Queen a ransom of £80,000. He went back to the Tower but was soon released to retire to Sherborne, where Guiana came gradually to fill his thoughts as a means of climbing out of obscurity into a blaze of achievement.

Very little is known about the preparation of Raleigh's expedition. He and his wife felt their exclusion from Court and from favour keenly. The earliest indication that Raleigh was considering a voyage was the letter which his wife wrote to Sir Robert Cecil on February 8, 1594, in which she said: 'I hope, for my sake, you will rather draw Sir Walter towards the east, than help him forward towards the sunset,' the implication being that Cecil could, if he pleased, do something to get Raleigh reinstated at Court.

During 1594 he sent out Captain Jacob

Whiddon, Sarmiento's captor and a privateer in Raleigh's service in 1590 as well as 1586, to Trinidad to spy out the situation there. He took his pinnace to the island and asked permission from the governor, Berrio, to take in wood and water, which was granted. He also tried to glean information on Guiana from him. Whiddon made a number of useful friends among the native caciques of the island, who were for the most part hostile to the Spanish occupants. But when he went to look for an English vessel reported to have arrived at an island harbour, Berrio seized the opportunity to weaken the crew left on board the pinnace. He sent a party of Indians out to invite them to come to hunt deer. Eight men agreed to do so, but they were ambushed on shore and killed by Berrio's men. Whiddon left the island very soon after this event, and though he may have picked up some tales about Guiana from the natives, his information does not appear to have been of much value. Yet on his return he gave Raleigh the impression that the hidden kingdom of El Dorado was to be found quite near the mainland coast.

Captain George Popham also contributed something to Raleigh's knowledge of Guiana. In 1594, while privateering in the Canaries, he had released from captivity a Captain Parker (or Harper), who had formerly been in Raleigh's service and who had some information and documents. Later, Popham acquired further documentary evidence on Guiana, probably on his way to Trinidad early in 1595. If the letters and the version of De Vera's report on his Orinoco voyage of 1593, published in 1596 by Raleigh, were among the papers captured in 1594, which is not certain, Raleigh was quite well posted on the state of the El Dorado search on his arrival at Trinidad in 1595.

While Whiddon and Popham were obtaining information on Guiana for him, Raleigh was engaged in trying to get Lord Charles Howard to put a fleet, with which Raleigh would sail, into the Channel to ward off threatening Spanish attacks, while he also advocated the smashing of a Spanish fort at Crozon which had been built for the reduction of the port of Brest. In August Raleigh was off the Kent coast on the Channel patrol, but he did not accompany the expedition which drove the Spaniards from Brittany in November. Even while he was at sea he must have had preparations under way for the Guiana expedition, which he intended to lead himself.

In these preparations he was assisted by Lord Charles Howard and Sir Robert Cecil. The Lord Admiral gave his ship, the *Lion's Whelp*, and Cecil must have contributed money. Raleigh says that he himself spent what little he had saved out of the wreck of his fortunes. A number of his relatives—his cousins, Butshead Gorges

179

and John Greville, Sir Richard's son, and his nephew, John Gilbert—were willing to adventure in person with him, and doubtless subscribed, with others of his friends, towards expenses. He could hope for no royal support and he knew the Spaniards were established in some force on Trinidad and might have been reinforced from Spain or from other established Spanish posts along this coast. While he might hope to deal, as he did, with Berrio's garrison with his own resources, there was a prospect of his having much more to meet.

He appears to have planned co-operation with a number of the privateers who ordinarily went to the West Indies early in the year. Some would work with him directly at Trinidad. Others would carry on as usual, but concentrate on the Spanish settlements to the west of the island. Popham and Sir Robert Dudley agreed to meet him at Trinidad in February. Amyas Preston and George Somers were going shortly afterwards and were expected to take part. Yet not every privateering leader was acceptable to Raleigh. He wrote irritably to Sir Robert Cecil in December:

'It is more than time that there be a restraint of all shipping bound out to the wars; for there are multitudes going for the Indies. If any men be taken (as some every year are) the Queen's purpose will be frustrated. And if Eaton's ships go, who will attempt the chiefest places of my enterprise, I shall be undone; and I know they will be beaten and do no good.'

However, with some hope that about a dozen ships would be available to meet any Spanish concentration, and knowing that Drake and Hawkins expected to deliver a great blow at Panama during 1595, Raleigh could proceed with his own preparations. As late as December 26, 1594, he hoped to put seven ships to sea but complained that they were still held up in the Thames by unfavourable winds. Probably they came round to a south-coast port shortly afterwards where Raleigh could join them from Sherborne. But only four vessels left for Guiana on February 6, 1595. One of his own ships, we do not know its name or tonnage, was admiral, Jacob Whiddon captain, John Douglas master. A small *gallego*, probably a Spanish prize, was under the command of Laurence Keymis, and a small bark was commanded first by Captain Cross and then, apparently, by Captain Robert Calfield. The vice-admiral was Howard's *Lion's Whelp*, Captain George Gifford. We have no figures of the total number that sailed. From Raleigh's narrative 300 would be a reasonable estimate, about half of whom were soldiers and adventurers.

On the transatlantic voyage Raleigh and Cross parted company with the *gallego* and the

Lion's Whelp, and delayed at the Canaries for over a week, awaiting them and Preston's vessels. Finally they sailed off alone, reaching Trinidad on March 22 and anchoring off Punto Gallo, now Icacos Point, at the south-west tip of the island.

There they probably expected to find Dudley and Popham, but missed them, owing to the delays about which Raleigh had complained. Dudley had reached the island on February 1 and was delighted with its appearance and excited by the prospects of exploring the Guiana mainland. He does not appear to have been molested by Berrio's men and he gained a certain amount of information from the natives about the mainland. Having sent two small vessels to pick up prizes, he took a pinnace into the Orinoco estuary and made contact with the mainland Indians, who told him the usual tales of El Dorado. He was away for sixteen days and claimed to have covered some 250 miles, but he does not give any details of his route. On his return he found that Popham had arrived, and they discussed renewing the search for a passage into the interior, but decided against it as Popham had lost his pinnaces. They waited only a week for Raleigh and, as he did not appear, went off privateering on March 12, ten days before Raleigh arrived. Raleigh's plan of co-operating with other privateers had broken down, Preston also failing him.

We have no account, written before he left England, of Raleigh's plans in 1595, but from his actions and his subsequent writings they are clear enough. His expedition was intended to spy out the strength of the Spaniards in the region, establish good relations with the Indians of Trinidad and the mainland, and attempt to find a route to Manoa, verify its riches and make an alliance with its people. He hoped that the Queen would send him back later with an official expedition to take possession of Guiana, with the consent and support of its inhabitants, so that it could form the nucleus of an English tropical empire which in time would surpass and finally subvert the Spanish empire in America.

The establishment of good relations with the natives was fundamental to success. Moral indignation at the cruelties of the Spaniards towards the native inhabitants in America had become, as we have seen, one principal item in English war propaganda against Spain. Ever since Drake and Oxenham, in the 'seventies, had co-operated with the Cimaroons of the isthmus against the Spaniards, the idea of finding allies among American natives or fugitive slaves had figured in plans for the ruin of the Spanish colonial dominion. The Spaniards were only beginning to penetrate Guiana, and the prospects of establishing friendly relations with the natives seemed good. Apart from El Dorado itself, the Indians of Trinidad and the Orinoco basin were not to be despised as allies. Their many gold ornaments suggested they knew where gold could be won, while the Trinidad people were already experienced traders. Besides, the natives held the entry or entries to Manoa. Their aid might make the difference between success and failure. Therefore Raleigh was anxious to take the initiative in penetrating Guiana rather than let it became a field open to the indiscriminate plunder of privateers who were certain to antagonize the Indians. Despite the crises between natives and settlers in Virginia, Raleigh did not envisage any difficulties in inducing Guiana Indians to accept an English protectorate and, subsequently, English colonists.

From his first landfall at Trinidad, Raleigh worked round by boat to rejoin the ships at Port of Spain. He made several landings and noted something of the island produce, especially the great pitch lake, which he believed could be exploited. Berrio had put a guard at the landing-place in the harbour, but his men proved friendly enough, as they came on board to buy linen and be pumped about El Dorado. Some of Whiddon's native acquaintances visited the ship and told of Spanish oppression and Berrio's order forbidding trade with the English. Raleigh decided to destroy the Spanish settlement and capture Berrio. He wished to revenge Whiddon's men and had heard Berrio had sent to Margarita and Cumana for reinforcements. Consequently, the harbour-guard was wiped out and Raleigh landed 100 men, who marched inland and surprised San Josef, meeting little resistance. The little town was burnt down, the Spaniards killed or dispersed, and Berrio and Captain Alvaro Jorge taken on board Raleigh's ship for interrogation. On the day the fort fell the *Lion's Whelp* and Keymis's *gallego* entered the harbour, and Raleigh could begin preparations for the journey into the interior.

He set his men to work to build a fort at Icacos Point, which could be used to ward off Spanish intervention, and he received much help in its construction from the natives. The Indians were delighted at the destruction of the Spanish settlement, and were apparently very tactfully handled by Raleigh. They brought in supplies and showed great friendliness. Later, Raleigh called a meeting of their caciques and explained that his Queen was the enemy of the Spaniards and would protect them. They apparently agreed to acknowledge the Queen as their ruler, and Raleigh formally annexed the island, erecting a high pole bearing the royal arms.

He was also preparing craft for the ascent of the Orinoco. Probably remembering the problems of the North Carolina coast, he had brought out the shallow-draught *gallego* for river-work. She was stripped, her upper works removed, and her hull re-equipped as a galley, so that she could be rowed upstream if winds were unfavourable. Parties were sent out to sound the many mouths of the Orinoco and returned to report that they could find no channel deep enough to take an ocean-going vessel. Finally, the galley and four boats were ready, with 100 men and provisions for a month.

Raleigh was no hardened explorer, and he found the comparatively easy trip up the river burdensome and undignified. He says that his company were:

> 'All driven to lie in the rain and weather, in the open air, in the burning sun, and upon the hard boards, and to dress our meat, and to carry all manner of furniture in them, wherewith they were so pestered and unsavoury, that what with victuals being most fish, with the wet clothes of so many men thrust together and the heat of the sun, I will undertake there was never any prison in England that could be found more unsavoury and loathsome, especially to myself, who had for many years before been dieted and cared for in a far sort differing.'

Raleigh was now much better informed about his route than on his arrival at Trinidad. He had treated his prisoners Berrio and Jorge well to begin with: the former was an old man of seventy-five, who told a good deal about the background of the search for Guiana and of his

own expeditions over the banquets Raleigh
gave him on board ship. Jorge, who had been on
Berrio's last expedition, reported a silver-mine
up the Caroni River. Berrio, however, strongly
advised against proceeding up the Orinoco in
search of Guiana. The rivers were too shallow
for even small boats, though in the summer
floods the current would be too swift, the Indians
would desert their villages on their approach
and, if found, would refuse to trade their gold.
These arguments were natural—and partly true
—but Raleigh was not deceived, though he
records they had some effect in discouraging his
men.

It took the expedition fifteen days, via the
Caño Manamo, through the delta, to reach the
broad stream of the great river, behind which
they could see at last the high escarpment of
the plateau rising to the south of the Orinoco.
Raleigh was not impressed by the 'broken
islands and drowned lands' and the 'woods,
prickles, bushes and thorns' of the delta's
tropical forest. Their Indian pilot had found
the passage difficult, but fortunately they
acquired a better guide, an old man kidnapped
from a native canoe. They ran short of food and
the old Indian led three boats up a branch of
the stream towards a village. The journey was
longer than Raleigh expected, and 'at the last,'
he says, 'we determined to hang the pilot,' but
before they did so he brought them to their

destination, and they traded some goods for bread, fish and hens. Here Raleigh had his first glimpse of a tract of the savannah country, typical of the Orinoco valley. He described it as 'the most beautiful country that ever mine eyes beheld. . . . here we beheld plains of twenty miles in length, the grass short and green, and in divers places groves of trees by themselves, as if they had been by all the art and labour in the world so made of purpose: and still as we rowed, the deer came down feeding by the water's side, as if they had been used to a keeper's call.' Food again went short until four canoes were encountered going down to Margarita with three Spaniards on board. The Spaniards got away, but two laden canoes were taken and another pilot seized. From him Raleigh learnt something of the Spaniards' attempts to pan gold from the streams.

After the expedition had passed from the delta into the main stream of the Orinoco, Raleigh began to develop his native policy, already tried out in Trinidad, on the South American mainland, as he made contact with the Indian caciques there. Here is his own description of his activities:

'I made them understand that I was a servant of a Queen, who was the great cacique of the north and a virgin . . . that she was an enemy to the *Castellani* [Spaniards] in respect of their tyranny and oppression, and that she delivered all such nations about her, as were by them oppressed, and having freed all the coast of the northern world from their servitude had sent me to free them also, and withal to defend the country of Guiana from their invasion and conquest. I showed them her majesty's picture which they so admired and honoured, as it had been easy to have brought them idolatrous thereof . . . so as in that part of the world her majesty is very famous and admirable, whom they now call *Ezrabeta Cassipuna Aquerewana*, which is as much as Elizabeth, the great princess or greatest commander.'

He tells us also that since the Spaniards had treated the Indians harshly and raided them for slaves, he was most careful to see that his men did not use force against them, molest their women or plunder their villages. 'But,' he said, 'I confess it was a very impatient work to keep the meaner sort from spoil and stealing, when we came to their houses, which because in all I could not prevent, I caused my Indian interpreter at every place when we departed, to know of the loss or wrong done, and if ought were stolen or taken by violence, either the same was restored, and the party punished in their sight, or else it was paid for to their uttermost demand.' He was also most anxious to hide from them his interest in gold. Consequently, he avoided trying to acquire any quantity of their gold ornaments, left their tombs unrifled and questioned them discreetly about mineral deposits. If they saw his main concern was gold, then they would conclude the English were not very different in their intentions from the Spaniards and would act accordingly. Instead, Raleigh handed out as presents gold coins 'with her majesty's picture to wear, with promise that they would become her servants thenceforth.' He received a number of promises of submission to the Queen and to himself as her lieutenant, and he gave assurances that he would come the following year with a large force to give them permanent protection against the Spaniards, which were reinforced by the spreading news of his liquidation of the Spanish hold on Trinidad.

The first cacique encountered was one Topari-maca, who took the party to his village, entertained them with native wine 'till they were reasonable pleasant,' gave Raleigh assurances of friendship and another pilot, and sped him along the great river:

> . . . four, five and six miles over in many places, and twenty miles in other places, with wonderful eddies, and strong currents, many great islands and divers shoals, and many dangerous rocks, and besides upon any increase of wind so great a billow, as we were sometimes in great peril of drowning in the galley, for the small boats durst not come from the shore, but when it was very fair.'

Travelling by day and anchoring by night, they arrived on the sixth day at the settlement of Morequito, and there Raleigh met the old chieftain Topiawari, overlord of the adjacent tribes. He had succeeded his nephew, Morequito, who had been killed by Berrio, and had himself suffered at the hands of the Spaniards, so that his reception of Raleigh's overtures was favourable. He supplied the expedition plentifully with food, and told Raleigh much about the Indian peoples and many tales about what lay behind the great escarpment. His story was of Indian wars and of the invasion of the plateau by 'a nation from so far off as the sun slept . . . with so great a multitude as they could not be numbered nor resisted, and that they wore large coats, and hats of crimson colour . . . and that they were called *Oreiones*, and *Epuremei*.' They had slain many of the old inhabitants and made themselves lords of most of the highland region, building 'a great town, *Macureguarai*, at the said mountain foot: and that their houses have many rooms, one over the other.' The incursion by a semi-civilized people into the highlands seems reasonably well established, but with what Raleigh had learnt from Berrio he was able to read much more into Topiawari's statement, for a little later in his narrative the *Epuremei* become 'subjects to *Inga*, emperor of Guiana and Manoa.'

The next day they set out to ascend the

Caroni, the tributary of the Orinoco by which Raleigh believed passage might be found through the escarpment. The boats could make no headway against the strong current at the mouth. The local cacique, one Wanuretona, was sent for, whom Raleigh treated as he had done Topiawari and who provided similar supplies and information, but with the additional emphasis on the wealth of the *Epuremei* in gold, and the hostility of the Caroni River peoples towards them. By this time all the rivers were rising fast with the summer rains, four or five feet, Raleigh said, and the increasing current, especially on the Caroni, rendered further progress by boat impossible. Raleigh therefore prepared three reconnaissance parties; one under Captain Thynne was to work overland towards the mountains to an Indian town called Capurepana, another under Captain Whiddon was to search the river banks for specimens of gold-bearing rock, while Raleigh himself set out with a party up the bank of the Caroni, and, though they did not proceed far, they saw enough to appreciate that it would not be possible with their resources to scale the falls, climb the deep gorge and reach the escarpment towering in the distance. He tells us:

'When we ran to the tops of the first hills of the plains adjoining to the river, we beheld that wonderful breach of waters, which ran down *Caroli* [Caroni]: and might from that mountain see the river how it ran in three parts, above twenty miles off, and there appeared some ten or twelve overfalls in sight, every one as high over the other as a church tower, which fell with that fury, that the rebound of waters made it seem as if it had been all covered over with a great shower of rain: and in some places we took it at the first for a smoke that had risen over some great town.'

The parties returned to the mouth of the Caroni and made preparations to return. Ralcigh says:

'I thought it time lost to linger any longer in that place, especially for that the fury of [the] Orinoco began daily to threaten us with dangers in our return, for no half day passed, but the river began to rage and overflow very fearfully, and the rains came down in terrible showers, and gusts in great abundance.'

The expedition rode down rapidly on the current to Morequito, and Raleigh again took counsel with Topiawari. The old chieftain, according to Raleigh's report, advised that it would be possible to go over the mountains, but only if Raleigh had a much stronger force to meet the armies of the Inca, with the alliance of the peoples on the fringes of the plateau whose help alone could enable an expedition to make headway. They discussed the possibility of reaching the nearest town of the

Epuremei—Macureguarai—with Raleigh's small force and some of Topiawari's men. But the old chief would not leave his settlements defenceless and Raleigh could not spare the fifty men he demanded should be left to guard them. Raleigh decided to abandon the project for the time being. He defends himself by saying that if he had made known his intention to invade the highlands and seize gold and sack cities, the Manoans might well have joined with the Spaniards, whereas 'if her majesty undertake the enterprize, they will rather submit themselves to her obedience than to the Spaniards of whose cruelty both themselves and the borderers have already tasted: and there till I had known her majesty's pleasure, I would rather have lost the sack of one or two towns . . . than to have defaced or endangered the future hope of so many millions, and the great good, and rich trade which England may be possessed thereby.'

Raleigh promised Topiawari to bring out a further expedition and left behind two Englishmen, Francis Sparrey and a boy, Hugh Goodwin, while Topiawari gave Raleigh his son to take to England. They parted, leaving Raleigh convinced that the people beyond the mountains formed the lost Inca empire of El Dorado, and Topiawari conscious only of a higher civilization there than his own which he needed help to plunder.

194

On the way to the delta Raleigh made a number of detours by land and water, and one party, under Captain Keymis, was told by the Indians of a gold-mine which was to form his principal objective in 1617. In rapidly worsening weather the boats reached and passed through the delta and rejoined the ships at Trinidad after a month's absence. Raleigh's expedition has no importance in the history of the exploration of the Orinoco, for his route was well known to the Spaniards. But he had brought Englishmen for the first time into the interior of South America, and had fixed in his own mind and that of a number of his men the burning desire to emulate the Spanish *conquistadores* of an earlier generation.

Surprisingly, in view of his earlier promises to the Indians there, Raleigh made no attempt to leave a garrison on Trinidad. He probably felt that no force he could spare would be of any value against the power the Spaniards could raise from the Spanish Main and expected from Europe. Surprisingly also, he released Berrio and Jorge, but he went on to attack Cumana. After initial successes, his men were driven back to their ships with very heavy losses. If raids on Rio de la Hacha and Santa Marta followed they were ineffective. Sailing back, Raleigh had thought to go to Virginia, but bad weather interfered and he proceeded homewards, arriving in England in September.

For Raleigh's own future everything depended on his ability to convince the Queen of the soundness of his speculations about El Dorado, now that he had reconnoitred Guiana in person. He had also to satisfy his backers at Court and investors throughout the country of the good prospects of a further expedition on a large scale. His reception on his return was evidently chilly: he must have been informed that he was still excluded from Court, and on November 10 he wrote despairingly to Sir Robert Cecil 'from this desolate place [Sherborne] I have little matter; from myself, less hope.' He went on to speak of Guiana:

> 'What becomes of Guiana I much desire to hear—whether it pass for a history or a fable. I hear Mr. Dudley and others are sending thither; if it be so, farewell all good from thence. For although myself—like a cockscomb—did rather prefer the future, in respect of others; and rather sought to win the kings to her majesty's service than to sack them, I know what others will do, when those kings shall come simply into their hands. If it may please you to acquaint my lord admiral therewith, let it then succeed as it will.'

Three days later he received a letter from Cecil which must have offered some slight prospects of a better hearing at Court, for he wrote back immediately, referring to a letter, taken by Popham from Domingo Martines of Jamaica, which mentioned a golden image supposedly taken from El Dorado and weighing some 47,000 pounds, which Raleigh estimated to be worth £100,000. 'I know,' said Raleigh optimistically, 'that in Manoa there are store of these.' He returned to emphasize his previous request that no privateers should be allowed to go to disturb the good relations established with the Indians. 'The like fortune was never offered to any Christian prince. I know,' he said, 'it will be presently followed both by the Spanish and French; and if it be foreslowed by us, I conclude that we are cursed of God. . . . If the Spaniards had been so blockish and slothful, we had not feared now their power, who by their gold from thence vex and endanger all the estates of kings. We must not look to maintain war upon the revenues of England. If we be once driven to the defensive, farewell might.' He was having Thomas Hariot make a map of Guiana for Cecil to present to the Queen, and was also getting cut various stones he had brought to England, 'but we must cast so many doubts; and this dolt and that gull must be satisfied, or else all is nothing.' His plea was 'I hope I shall be thought worthy to direct those actions that I have at mine own charges laboured in; and to govern that country which I have discovered, and hope to conquer for the Queen without her cost.' If he was thought unworthy he wished the Queen to commission a better man to carry out his project.

His miscellaneous specimens of ore and presumably precious stones contributed to the growing scepticism. Rumour said he had not, himself, accompanied the ships to Guiana, but had acquired in Barbary the supposed Orinoco gold. He got more and more impatient. 'I beseech you,' he wrote to Cecil towards the end of November, 'let us know whether we shall be travellers, or tinkers; conquerors, or novices. For if the winter pass without making provision, there can be no victualling in the summer; and if it be now foreslowed, farewell Guiana for ever. Then must I determine to beg or run away. Honour, and gold, and all good, for ever hopeless.'

He settled down to write his report on his voyage and a plea for its continuance. This was addressed to the Lord Admiral and Sir Robert Cecil in an eloquent repudiation of the aspersions cast on his objectives and his actions on the voyage. When it was completed it must have been clear to Raleigh that no royal help could immediately be expected, and so, in spite of the indications it would give the Spaniards, he published it as *The Discoverie of the Large Rich, and Bewtiful Empyre of Guiana* in 1596. His narrative is the main source of information on the expedition of 1595. For the greedy he stressed the favourable assays made of the ore brought home, but the core of the book is its plea for official English intervention in Guiana.

He proclaimed his belief in the Inca empire of El Dorado, but asserted the desirability of controlling the whole of the Orinoco valley as well as the Guiana highlands. The main incentive is spoil: 'The common soldier shall here fight for gold, and pay himself, instead of pence, with plates of half a foot broad, whereas he breaketh his bones in other wars for provender and penury.' The country was healthy for explorers or settlers. There was plenty of game and, besides gold, there was valuable timber, dye-stuffs, cotton, silk, balsam, gums and pepper to be had near the mouth of the Orinoco, and good soil for plantation-crops of sugar and ginger. The sea passage was easy, and the territory, once conquered, easily defensible. He, himself, had driven the Spaniards from their foothold and won many peoples there to friendship with England. A small force sent to Manoa would be sufficient to force the Inca to pay tribute and maintain an English garrison to defend him against Spain. The Queen could employ there all the 'soldiers and gentlemen that are younger brethren, and all captains and chieftains that want employment.' The only charge would be to despatch them armed and victualled for a year, 'for after the first or second year I doubt not but to see in London a *contratación* house of more receipt for Guiana, than there is now in Seville for the West Indies,' 'To conclude,' he said, 'Guiana is a country that hath yet her

199

maidenhead, never sacked, turned, nor wrought, the face of the earth hath not been torn, nor the virtue and salt of the soil spent by manurance, the graves have not been opened for gold, the mines not broken with sledges, nor their images pulled down out of their temples.'

Raleigh was prepared to pledge himself to pursue the project to the end of his resources:

'I hope it shall appear that there is a way found to answer every man's longing, a better Indies for her majesty than the king of Spain hath any, which if it shall please her highness to undertake, I shall most willingly end the rest of my days in following the same.'

His eloquence, the profusion of incentives, with the appeals alike to private greed and state necessity, joined to humanitarian motives in launching a native policy superior to that of Spain, testify to his single-mindedness, but also make his statesmanship somewhat suspect. The prospect is too lush: the *Discoverie* leaves the reader with the feeling that Raleigh, in spite of his protestations to the contrary, was more desperate for personal glory and plunder than for the welfare of natives, his fellow-adventurers or the English state. Though this impression would be, in an appreciable degree, unjust to Raleigh, the *Discoverie* aroused much interest in, though little support for, a project for which he had rather over-stated his case.

Another treatise, *Of the Voyage for Guiana*, not published at the time, sets out the objectives Raleigh sought in the conquest of Guiana more systematically, even though it is more likely to be by Keymis or by Thomas Hariot than by Raleigh himself. It argues that it will be honourable, profitable, necessary, cheap and easy to acquire Guiana—honourable from the conversion of millions of heathen to Christianity and their preservation from Spanish tyranny; profitable from gold and jewels and, possibly, the ultimate capture of Peru; necessary because the Spaniards, strengthened by possession of Guiana, would be the more dangerous to England; easy since the alliance of the natives against the Spaniards was assured, the voyage easy and the country easily defended.

The writer emphasized the advantages of maintaining the emperor of Guiana as a tributary to the English Crown because he could be used as an instrument for civilizing the natives, and summarizes 'the offers to be made to the Guianians' as:

'First that we will defend them. . . .
2. Then that we will help them to recover their country of Peru.
3. That we will instruct them in liberal arts of civility. . . .
4. And lastly that we will teach them the use of weapons . . . for service in the wars.'

This document, together with the *Discoverie*, presents for the first time an English colonial policy for a tropical colony, concerned primarily with using the native peoples, rather than English settlers, though they too would be needed for the benefit of the imperialist country. It is not very important that no semi-civilised empire of Guiana existed on which it might be tried, or that Elizabeth had no intention of attempting it. The idea of a colonial empire, utilizing a self-interested benevolence towards native peoples, was one of Raleigh's important contributions to English colonial theory.

The practical efforts which Raleigh made after 1595 to follow up his voyage were limited by his failure to entice either the Queen or any considerable body of private adventurers to follow the glittering trail. Yet he did his best. As early as November 13, 1595, he told Cecil: 'I am sending away a bark to the country to comfort and assure the people, that they despair not, nor yield to any composition with other nations.' Cecil and his aged father, Burghley, both contributed to send out Laurence Keymis with two ships in January 1596. Raleigh had begun to have doubts whether the interior of the plateau and his Lake Manoa could be reached by way of that part of the escarpment bordering the Orinoco Basin. Keymis was to work along the coast from the mouth of the Amazon towards the Orinoco and to inquire what were the best

passages into the interior highland. He succeeded in learning from the natives at the mouth
of the Essequibo, one of the many rivers flowing
north into the Atlantic, that by following the
river to its source and making a short portage
a great lake, called Parima, would be found.
This lake did exist as an inundation of the
savannah during the rainy season, and it seemed
to Keymis and Raleigh that it was Manoa. From
the Essequibo Keymis went on to the Orinoco.
His task there was to reassure the natives that
Raleigh would return soon, and also to obtain
some more convincing gold ore to confound the
many English doubters of Raleigh's claims about
the mineral wealth of the region. He found a
deeper and easier channel through the delta and
arrived at Morequito, but there he found that
Berrio had already established a small fortified
settlement, San Thomé, at the mouth of the
Caroni. The route up the Caroni was barred,
old Topiawari was dead and there was no chance
for Keymis to pick up gold near his old settlement.
Keymis sailed away just in time to miss a great
colonizing expedition from Spain under de Vera,
which was about to make a tragic failure of
populating the Orinoco Basin with Europeans.
The English ships got home at the end of June
with no gold and bad news of Spanish activities,
but with some new prospects of a route up the
Essequibo. Raleigh was not at home to greet
them.

He had, for the first time since his disgrace, received orders to take part in an important state venture. His voyage to Guiana had shown him to be a man of action, and, if the Queen was not prepared to back him in his project of empire, yet she forgave him something. Thus he left Plymouth on June 7 as vice-admiral of the great fleet, under the Lord Admiral and Essex, which was bound for Cadiz. Largely responsible for the decision to attack from the sea before making a landing, he commanded the vanguard and himself attacked the great galleons which had smashed the *Revenge* in 1591. Two were taken and the rest burned. Wounded in the leg, he could take no active part in the landing and sack of the city. His courage and skill had won him honour and another round in his struggle for rehabilitation, but, as usual, he complained that he had not obtained wealth as well, his share in the spoil being only £1,769. He arrived back in England on August 6.

Meantime his wife had been telling Cecil of Keymis's bad news of the Orinoco, and saying of her husband that 'if he had been as well credited in his reports and knowledges as it seemeth the Spaniards were they had not now been possessors of that place.' Thomas Hariot, too, wrote to Cecil of his work on Raleigh's papers and maps, and urged that maps and books be taken from two indiscreet companions of Keymis, Samuel Mace and William Downe, because 'if it shall please her majesty to undertake the enterprise, or permit it in her subjects, by her order, countenance and authority, for the supplanting of those that are now gotten thither, I think it of great importance to keep that which is done as secretly as we may.' Cecil agreed and made the seamen hand over the documents for safe keeping. Keymis wrote a narrative of his voyage, however, and made another strong plea for English action. He said that his second visit had confirmed his belief in the prospects of Guiana and in the ease with which English power could be established, possibly by private adventurers (though they would tend to plunder and depart) and certainly by the state.

Raleigh's own belief in the project held firm. He was greatly attracted by Keymis's news of the great lake accessible from the Essequibo, and on December 27, 1596, he despatched Captain Leonard Berry with the pinnace *Watte* to follow up the discoveries. Berry explored three of the rivers which flowed into the Atlantic—the Wiapoco (now Oyapoc), Marawyne and Corentyne— up to the point where they left the highlands. Keymis had already done propaganda for Raleigh among the natives and Berry continued his work, finding them well disposed and leaving them with news that Raleigh would soon arrive to attempt the plateau. His report gave encouraging prospects of reaching Lake Parima, but he, too, on his return found Raleigh busy on royal service. Raleigh's part in the Cadiz expedition paved the way for a return to Court. A somewhat superficial reconciliation was effected with Essex, and on June 1 Elizabeth received him and took him back into her immediate circle. Finally, in July, he set out under Essex's command as rear-admiral of a fleet designed to attack Ferrol, capture and garrison the Azores and intercept the American trading and treasure fleets. The Islands Voyage was very much a fiasco. Bad weather delayed the departure of the fleet; the attack on Ferrol proved impracticable; Raleigh and Essex quarrelled over the former's raid on Fayal; the attack on Terceira was abandoned; the American fleet escaped, except for a small number of prizes, in the profits of which Raleigh shared.

Between 1595 and 1597 Raleigh had the satisfaction of seeing offensive action against Spain stepped up, but the Islands Voyage was the last great expedition of the Tudor period. The war gradually fizzled out. Raleigh became absorbed in a multitude of royal duties, and received no encouragement to revive his Guiana project. In 1598 he was said to be preparing, in co-operation with Sir John Gilbert, a fleet of pinnaces to transport, not an army but a body of settlers to the Guiana coast. He made an abortive attempt to get aid from a Swedish prince. The indications are that his thoughts were turning from El Dorado towards the colonization of the coastlands with English settlers, whose relations with the natives would be carefully regulated. He did not find the support, time or money to proceed, but he did stimulate English traders to make further commercial contacts with the Amazon-Orinoco zone, and he aroused the interest of both French and Dutch in the area. He laid the foundations for the smaller colonizing attempts by English adventurers which began in 1602. But his conception of tropical colonization was his important contribution to English expansion, even though it found no support from the state.

The weakness of the colonizing movement in England in Elizabeth's reign has already been illustrated from North America. The reluctance to plunge into empire in South America sprang from similar motives. The Queen and her advisers shrank from any overseas enterprise which would use up continuous supplies of capital, shipping and men over a considerable period. El Dorado was not sufficiently well-attested for the state to make the great gamble which Raleigh proposed, nor did it attract a wide enough circle of private speculators. The other prospects—dominion over the Orinoco and Guiana Lowland Indians and the building of plantation colonies—were speculations of the same order as that of settling Europeans in Virginia. English expansion in the latter half of the sixteenth century was carried on effectively only by terminable joint-stock ventures. Whether for privateering or for voyages to the Levant or to Asia, such ventures might get royal as well as private support. If they succeeded, they paid dividends; if they failed, they lost money only to the subscribers and did not involve a long-continued drain on private or public funds. The total results which they achieved in plunder and trade were extremely important in the building up of a capitalist economy in England, but their method was not suited to colonization. Raleigh was in the main stream of the expansion movement of his own time when he speculated in privateering ventures. He was a pioneer when he tried to use similar methods for the building up of colonies overseas, and his failures taught his successors many lessons. For all the daring attacks made on Spanish power, her great wealth and resources made the Crown hesitate about committing all its resources in an attempt to take over the Spanish empire. Raleigh was among the most strenuous advocates of such an attempt, and it was probably fortunate for the future prospects of English expansion that he failed.

Chapter Seven

The Refounding of Virginia

ALL that Raleigh had salved from the wreck of the first three American colonies was a legal title. Under the patent of 1584 he held the prior right to 1,200 miles of the coast and the hinterland so long as he could claim to have established a colony in some part of it before 1591. Though White's colony had been lost sight of in 1587, there was no proof that it was not still in existence, and its presumed continuance in America enabled Raleigh to revive his claims and to renew his expeditions after the turn of the century.

According to his *Discoverie of Guiana*, Raleigh told the Spaniards on his arrival at Trinidad in 1595, 'that I was bound only for the relief of those English which I had planted in Virginia.' The Spanish version was that 'he also mentioned that he had founded a town in Canaveral on the coast of Florida, and that he only came to the port to get wood which he needed, and to carry weapons and ammunition to the English who were in the Canaveral.' Raleigh assures his readers that his intention to visit Virginia was genuine, 'which I had performed in my return if extremity of weather had not forced me from the said coast.' But his pre-occupation first with Guiana and then with the naval warfare against the Spaniards and a variety of duties at Court all combined to divert his attention from North America. Thus, between 1591 and 1602, there is no certain record of any English voyages to the American coast from New England southward.

The Spanish war did much to hold back English exploitation of the American mainland, yet between 1591 and 1598 knowledge of the northern part of the mainland was extended. Merchants were sending ships to fish off Cape Breton, and these did an intermittent trade with the local Indians. Other vessels were pushing into the Gulf of St. Lawrence and, besides fishing, hunted walrus and whales. In 1591 Thomas James of Bristol reported to Burghley the 'discovery of the island of Ramea' in the St. Lawrence, and it was visited again 1593 by George Drake of Topsham and in 1597 by Charles Leigh. In 1594 a Bristol ship visited Anticosti. Many other expeditions have gone unrecorded, but it is clear that the English were following the French and Spanish vessels, which had been the pioneers in fishing these waters.

A colony was projected on Ramea, but little is known about it. Early in 1597 a group of non-conformists, 'falsely called Brownists' as they said, petitioned the Privy Council, proclaiming

210

their loyalty to the Crown, in spite of which they had been persecuted at home and driven abroad. They asked permission to remove to Ramea, where they might exercise freedom of worship. The Privy Council acceded to this request on March 25, after investigation. An advance party of four was to leave in two vessels which were going fishing in the St. Lawrence, supplied by Alexander van Harwick and Charles Leigh, merchants of London. They were to winter on the island with one ship, and in the following year the whole group might be allowed to follow, provided they did not return to England without conforming to the Established Church. The *Hopewell* and the *Chancewell* set out in April. Leigh took the former to Ramea, but he left neither ship nor pioneers there, and his vessels fought with some French and Spanish competitors, did some fishing, traded with the Cape Breton Indians and returned in September. In November the Privy Council still believed that an expedition would sail the following year, and released an imprisoned Brownist on that account. But the project was dropped, apparently because Leigh reported that Basques and Bretons were too strong and hostile to permit the establishment of any English base in this area.

In 1598, however, Richard Hakluyt began the publication of the second, and greatly enlarged, edition of the *Principal Navigations* as an incentive to further English overseas enterprise. In the same year he gave it as his opinion that White's colony still survived in Virginia, and in 1599 he urged Sir Robert Cecil in the epistle to his second volume to sponsor the revival of the Virginia enterprise. 'Not to meddle with the state of Ireland, nor that of Guiana,' he said, 'there is under our noses the great and ample country of Virginia'—thus linking the three objectives of the Elizabethan colonizing movement. He renewed his old argument that the state should take the initiative. 'Which action,' he said, 'if upon a good and godly peace obtained, it shall please the Almighty to stir up her majesty's heart to continue with her favourable countenance . . . with transporting of one or two thousand of her people . . . she shall by God's assistance, in short space, work many great and unlooked-for effects, increase her dominions, enrich her coffers, and reduce many pagans to the faith of Christ.' He was anxious to refocus attention on what appeared to him to be the main stream of English colonizing enterprise, 'my western Atlantis or America.'

Raleigh and others were inclined to agree with Hakluyt, and as the Spanish war died down expeditions to the North American coast were begun again. It is not clear when Raleigh revived the attempt to find White's lost colonists. Before 1602, he said, he had twice unsuccessfully sent vessels to the American coast under Captain Samuel Mace, though he did not renew trade in North American produce. In 1602 he despatched two vessels, one a pinnace, under Mace, to work up the coast to possible sites and also to trade. Mace reached the coast some 120 miles south of Cape Hatteras, to the north of Cape Fear, and landed there to trade with the Indians and to collect timber and medicinal plants. He loaded some sassafras wood and china root, a kind of sarsaparilla, both of which had come into great demand for the treatment of syphilis. Sassafras, which was then fetching 3s. to 20s. a pound in London, has no medicinal value, but sarsaparilla has. Other things collected were benjamin, *cassia lignea* (a cinnamon-like bark) and a spicy bark, mentioned by Hariot, apart from commodities obtained from the Indians. After staying for a month they left to work up the coast and, we are told:

> 'should have sought the people, both in the islands and upon the main, in divers appointed places, [but] they did it not, pretending that the extremity of weather and loss of some principal ground tackling forced and feared them from searching the port of Hatteras, the isle of Croatan, or any part of the main of Dasamonquepeuk.'

Sufficient cargo was brought back to Weymouth by August to pay for the cost of the expedition. Raleigh was in this way cautiously rebuilding his contacts with America on a strictly commercial basis.

At the same time there was a revival of interest in Humphrey Gilbert's Norumbega, which came to be known as North Virginia and later as New England. On March 26, 1602, Bartholomew Gosnold, Bartholomew Gilbert and John Brereton set out to establish an outpost there. Little is known about the persons or organization behind the voyage, which was intended to leave twenty settlers behind to prepare the way for a larger expedition. They sailed via the Azores, made their landfall on May 14 probably at Cape Neddick, Maine, and coasted southwards, collecting furs and skins from the Indians and loading some sassafras and cedar trees where they landed. They chose a small island, Cuttyhunk, south of Massachusetts, which they named Elizabeth's Isle, as their base, and proceeded to erect a small fort. As so often happened on these early expeditions, they found the stores they could leave insufficient to assure reasonable safety to the settlers. There were quarrels; finally, on June 18, the whole expedition sailed for home, arriving on July 23. Brereton and his associates were enthusiastic about the prospects of North Virginia, in spite of the difficulties they met. Raleigh encountered Bartholomew Gilbert at Weymouth and learnt, apparently for the first time, of the voyage. Half angry and half glad, Raleigh's immediate concern was lest the sassafras brought back would flood the market and so lower his own receipts from the voyage to South Virignia. Gilbert proved willing to co-operate, and Raleigh sent him to Cecil with a letter, dated August 21, asking to have the sassafras impounded and the cedar seized. He reminded Cecil: 'I have a patent that all ships and goods are confiscate that shall trade there without my leave. . . . Gilbert went without my leave, and therefore *all* is confiscate.' In view of Gilbert's co-operation, he added 'he shall have his part again.' It was in this letter that Raleigh made his famous prophecy about Virginia—'I shall yet live to see it an English nation.'

The difficulty between Raleigh and the Brereton-Gilbert group was soon resolved, and Brereton published at the end of the year his *Briefe and True Relation of the Discoverie of the North Part of Virginia*, with a friendly dedication to Raleigh. It was the first piece of direct propaganda for American colonization for some years, and it ran through two impressions before the end of March 1603. It was probably agreed that further expeditions by this group should be made with Raleigh's permission. Their project was, however, taken up by Richard Hakluyt, who interested a wealthy group of Bristol merchants in it and received a licence from Raleigh to send out ships. The expedition did not set sail until April 1603, after Queen Elizabeth had died. Martin Pring took two vessels over the route previously followed by Gosnold and Gilbert, making a more intensive examination of the coast, trading with the Indians, and loading sassafras and cedar. One ship was sent home with a cargo, and the other stayed on until August and returned safely in October. The voyage, which had clarified the available knowledge about this region, probably paid its way.

In 1602 Raleigh had proposed to send out Mace again in 1603 with two ships, but it was Bartholomew Gilbert he chose to make a voyage to the Chesapeake. Leaving England on May 10, Gilbert worked his way round by the Canaries and West Indies, and up the American coast. He tried unsuccessfully to find his way into the Chesapeake, so he landed near the opening and was killed by the Indians. This discouraged his crew, and they sailed home in September. This was the last expedition Raleigh sent to Virginia; when it returned he was in the Tower charged with high treason. Taken with the recent voyages to the St. Lawrence area, these small expeditions, modest, commercial and realistic, performed a valuable service in arousing interest once again in America and in soothing fears of the impracticability of the voyage there. They played an essential part in preparing the way for a permanent colony in the next few years.

The new century brings a different atmo-

sphere into England's overseas effort. The sixteenth century had been distinguished by a
number of daring small-scale ventures, by much
experiment and speculation, and by almost
complete failure in constructive activities which
required continuous, large-scale planning and
did not bring in quick returns. In 1600 there
was still no permanent English foothold,
whether settlements or trading-posts, outside
Europe, though a great deal of experience had
been accumulated in the previous half-century.
Spanish power had overshadowed England
throughout Elizabeth's reign, inciting the more
adventurous seamen and investors to attack her
overseas and to challenge her imperial power,
but holding back the more cautious or fearful,
and diverting money and effort into essential
defences against her on sea and land. That
threat was lifting at the opening of the seventeenth century, and though Spain remained
powerful enough to defend her empire in the
west and to act as a great power in Europe, she
became a much weaker obstacle to large-scale
English overseas effort. The decline in her fortunes was best seen in her failure to protect the
Portuguese monopoly of trade with Asia, which
she held, from the onslaughts either of the
English or Dutch East India Companies, who
were able in the first quarter of the century to
lay firm foundations for a commercial empire
there.

Within the British Isles the union of the Crowns and the completion of the conquest of Ireland appeared to mark the final achievement of the Tudor objective of domestic consolidation, and it gave confidence and impetus to extra-European activity. Thus it proved possible in James I's reign to do many things which had proved impossible under Elizabeth—to colonize Ulster, Virginia and Bermuda and to begin the settlement of New England and Newfoundland. These things were not achieved by any great co-ordinated state effort or without further failures, but they were done on a scale which brought a measure of success denied to the Elizabethans. The slow quantitative development of English capitalism was producing a qualitative change in English society and enterprise. The growth of both industrial and commercial enterprises, through the accumulation of capital, the establishment of relatively powerful heavy industries, including shipbuilding, was transforming the middle-classes, making them more powerful and more self-reliant. New sources of raw materials, of new markets, of new settlements for Englishmen outside Great Britain, were pursued with more purposeful vigour and with more adequate resources. At home, though the Stuart monarchy continued to direct the policy and administration of the country, challenges to its claims to do so without regard to the interests of the middle-classes became open and widespread, and already under James royal intransigence was creating the conditions for a political revolution.

Raleigh could take little direct part in the developments of the new reign. For twenty-five years before Elizabeth's death he had been concerned with most aspects of the drive overseas: for the greater part of that time he was in a position of influence at Court and in the administration. For fifteen years of the new reign he survived, no less active mentally, no less anxious and able to take a prominent part in the overseas and internal affairs of the state, but forced by circumstances and the new monarch to take a side seat in prison, to know of most of the great developments of the age intimately, to feel them acutely, but not to act in any of them except the last adventure to Guiana, which cost him his life.

The years from 1597 to 1603 had been in many respects the fullest and most satisfying in Raleigh's public career. He retained throughout the close friendship of the ageing Queen. He was constantly consulted on matters of state and entrusted with special diplomatic and administrative tasks. As captain of the guard he was prominent at Court. Yet he was never allowed continuous responsibility for any large sphere of policy, and he never obtained admission to the Privy Council. As governor of Jersey from 1600 to 1603 he had some experience of ad-

ministering a small detached dominion of the
Crown, and he took his duties seriously and
spent much time there; but this was not an
appointment of political importance. It brought
him once again into contact with the Newfoundland fishery business, in which the islanders
were engaged: otherwise it had no effect on his
domestic or overseas activities. Though his
wisdom in counsel was respected by many ad-
ministrators and appreciated by the Queen, she
never seriously considered him as a major civil
servant or maker of policy. He was, for one
thing, too capable of seeing the many sides of a
controversial issue, and this led him to oppose
in Parliament certain aspects of royal trade,
taxation and ecclesiastical policy. His capacity
to play the part of the courtly flatterer was
limited by a refusal to conceal his deep intellectual contempt for artifice and policy. He had,
in fact, only a very limited capacity for working
in apparent friendliness with men he despised.
His 'bloody pride' was notorious and was an
insuperable obstacle to co-operation with those
he thought his inferiors if he should be given
really extensive responsibilities. His greed for
monetary rewards was rather blatant even for
his own time. There are very strange contrasts
in his character—especially between the contem-
plative man giving a shrewd, cool and far-
sighted opinion on some matter of state and the
haughty, intolerant figure of the proud courtier.

Elizabeth saw how to make use of his abilities without entrusting him with too much power.

These last six years of the Tudor period saw him make many powerful enemies. With Essex he was almost continuously at enmity. Essex had not a tithe of Raleigh's brains, but he had even more arrogance and self-assurance. He would tolerate no one at his side in his attempt to be the Queen's only mentor. Lacking Raleigh's ultimate contempt for long-continued scheming and party-making, he did build up a powerful military and aristocratic following and, as relations between the two went from bad to worse, he came to imagine that Raleigh was the main obstacle between him and complete domination of the state, so his followers came to detest Raleigh too. When, mad with thwarted ambition, Essex embarked on his crazy rising and was crushed and executed, Raleigh appeared to a wide public outside the Court as the sinister figure who had tricked and hounded a more brilliant man to disaster.

But behind the scenes Raleigh's downfall was being arranged. Elizabeth steadily refused public acknowledgment of James as her successor. Raleigh supported her for reasons of policy. Her ministers pretended to do so too, but most of them took out an insurance policy by entering into secret relations with James, promising him their aid and giving him their picture of the situation at the English Court.

221

Essex had done so, and his fall, at Raleigh's hand, as James was told, appeared a major disaster. Most assiduously Sir Robert Cecil had done so. While Essex had fought furiously for pride of place in the government, Cecil had grasped all the strings of administration and policy. Superficially he and Raleigh got on very well, and Raleigh was inclined to trust him as much as anyone in high place. But behind his back Cecil, among others, was building up for James a portrait of Raleigh as the master-schemer who he could believe might support the insignificant Arabella Stuart or even the Infanta as a means to power at Elizabeth's death.

So Raleigh, in that last year of Elizabeth's reign when he was again finding opportunity to revive his American projects, was standing on the edge of an abyss. He was surprised when James showed his distrust by including his patent to issue wine licences among the monopolies suspended early in May, 1603, and still more so when he was deprived of his Court office as captain of the guard, and a little later told to move out of Durham House, which had for long been his London residence. Yet he was not stripped of his Devon, Cornish and Jersey offices, and he remained at Court, endeavouring to show his good disposition towards the new monarch, without apparently showing any great resentment, until the middle of July. He endeavoured to win James's interest by offering him a discourse urging the continuance of the maritime war against Spain and of the alliance with the Dutch. This, however, was calculated to do more harm than good. James disliked the Dutch as rebels against lawful authority, he saw no reason why England any more than Scotland should fight with Spain, and he desired European peace. For all these reasons Raleigh's policy of continued war was obnoxious to him and helped to confirm his suspicions and dislike.

In the middle of July Raleigh was brought before the Privy Council and interrogated, a few days later placed under house-arrest and then removed to the Tower under a charge of high treason. No account can be given here of the tortuous conspiracies in which his enemies, the king's ministers, involved him. Briefly, it appears that at some time he had listened to his old friend Lord Cobham suggesting that Arabella Stuart, not James, should be placed on the English throne. Further, he had heard Cobham talk of pensions that had been promised by Count Aremberg, representative of the Spanish Netherlands, if a number of prominent personalities at Court helped to bring about a peace with Spain. Cobham was a silly schemer and some of his dealings with Aremberg had probably been treasonable, but they can scarcely have been directed in favour of Arabella Stuart against James, since Spain had her own candidate, the Infanta, for the throne; unless, indeed, Cobham decided to accept money from Spain and to use it for Anti-Spanish ends. However, when interrogated, Cobham claimed that anything he had done had been at Raleigh's instigation, though Raleigh subsequently got him to write an exonerating letter.

The government pressed on preparations for a treason trial, to be held at Winchester, and with Raleigh as the first defendant. In the meantime he had to surrender, or was deprived of, all his offices. The trial, which began on November 17, ended with a verdict of guilty. The indictment was to the effect that he and Cobham had conspired with Spain to place Arabella on the throne and to receive money for this purpose on condition that, after the success of the plot, peace would be made with Spain, the English Catholics tolerated and Arabella's marriage arranged by Spain. There were also charges that Raleigh had spoken treasonable words against the King and his children. Sir Edward Coke, as attorney-general, prosecuted in a long polemic against Raleigh. His main evidence consisted of unauthenticated depositions, none of which was conclusive, one witness to retail hearsay evidence, and a further statement by Cobham alleging, after all, that Raleigh had instigated him to get money out of Aremberg. This amounted to evidence about relations with Aremberg but none about the presumed

Arabella Stuart plot. Raleigh could not call witnesses nor council, but he replied to Coke's bitter denunciations with spirit: 'I was never false to the crown of England. I have spent £40,000 of my own against the Spanish faction for the good of my country,' he declared emphatically. Yet the lord chief justice, Sir John Popham, who was soon to take up Raleigh's old Virginia enterprise, ordered the jury to find him guilty, and they did. Cobham and two of his associates were similary convicted. All four were reprieved by the King at the last moment.

It is very hard to understand the trial and verdict in the light of modern legal practice.[1] James, Cecil and the rest acted as if they were convinced of Raleigh's guilt, and that was enough to satisfy the Court. Henry VIII had many men executed on even less evidence. By convicting Raleigh, James had the satisfaction of removing with the uttermost ignominy a personality whom he feared and disliked. He had given notice that vengeance would be taken against any plotters against his own security. He had, in spite of the nature of the charges, shown the Spaniards that he had broken with the man who had stood most prominently for the old policy of hostility to Spain, and he was able to make peace in 1604.

Raleigh was allowed to live on in the Tower

[1] J. Bruce Williamson, *Sir Walter Raleigh and his Trial* (1936).

225

for over twelve years. James's clemency is as hard to understand as his harshness, though the trial had turned much popular hatred into admiration, and he may have thought it unwise to make Raleigh a popular martyr. The Queen's intercession may have had some effect. In the Tower Raleigh led a curious life, able to meet with many of his friends and maintain a household on what James had left him after the legal seizure of his estate. He remained constantly hopeful of pardon and release, and won the friendship of the Queen and of young Prince Henry, who frequently visited him. He wrote much, principally the massive first volume of the *Historie of the World*, into which he put a good deal of learning and fine writing. His critical and sceptical intellect attacked many idols, and denounced those rulers who abused their power for tyrannical ends. Many of his asides and comments on his own time are acute and revealing; a number of them reiterate his hostility to Spain. He engaged in chemical experiments and compounded drugs. An ageing man, he kept closely in touch with contemporary politics and, especially, with the new overseas developments, Guiana obsessed him as a possible instrument for his release. Virginia continued to interest him as new efforts were made to establish a settlement there.

Raleigh's conviction had deprived him of the rights over the American shore that he had held himself entitled to as late as 1603. They reverted to the Crown, which might grant them as it wished. James, in the first years of his reign, desired to keep peace with Spain. In the treaty of London he had failed to get permission for his subjects to trade with the Spanish colonies; he had likewise refused to promise to respect the old Spanish claim to complete monopoly of commerce outside Europe. He opposed privateering and piracy, though he did not succeed in rooting out the latter; he did not attempt to stop English merchants attempting to trade with the East or West Indies if they could do so without too much violence. He remained quite consistent in refusing to admit the Spaniards had any overseas territorial rights except where they could prove effective occupation. This was in line with Tudor policy, and it was the basis on which he issued patents for colonizing purposes in North America, Bermuda, some of the Caribbean islands and Guiana.

Though Raleigh had no active share in the launching of the first permanent colony in America, there is a strong thread of continuity linking him to it. In the years 1603 to 1606 four groups of men focused their attention on the old problem of establishing colonies. First there were the London merchants who still survived from Raleigh's grantees of 1589. Head and shoulders above all the other merchants associated in overseas commerce and vitally concerned

227

with the East India, Muscovy and Levant Companies was now Sir Thomas Smythe. It was he who gathered the London companies round the enterprise and himself played a large part in its direction. Merchant interests were to a great extent concerned to develop imports such as timber and ships' stores, from America. Second, there was the Plymouth group, including Sir Humphrey Gilbert's sons, Sir John Popham and Sir Ferdinando Gorges, governor of Plymouth, whose interests were chiefly in the trade and fisheries of North Virginia. Third, there were the Bristol merchants, collected by Richard Hakluyt round Pring's venture in 1603. Hakluyt, as one of the original London grantees, acted as the link between the two merchant groups. Fourth, there was a new project for a Catholic colony. The Earl of Southampton sponsored the first voyage made after Raleigh's imprisonment by George Waymouth in 1605 in order to find a site for such a colony. This scheme was dropped when the Gunpowder plot forced the Catholics to lie low, but enthusiastic reports published by James Rosier on his return helped to stimulate interest in the project in Plymouth and elsewhere.

Through Popham, Gorges, and possibly with the encouragement of Sir Robert Cecil, now Earl of Salisbury, the remaining three groups were joined to petition for a royal charter for two closely associated companies, that of Plymouth to exploit North Virginia and that of London, with Bristol participating, South Virginia. The names of the signatories included Hakluyt and Raleigh Gilbert, Sir Humphrey's son. It may have been at this preparatory stage that Sir Walter Raleigh from his prison made a bid to take part in the new venture. In a letter written to Queen Anne, probably in 1610, he recalls:

'I long since presumed to offer your majesty my service in Virginia, with short repetition of the commodity, honour and safety which the king's majesty might reap by that plantation, if it were followed to effect.'

His offer was not accepted, and the documents concerning it do not appear to have survived.

The Virginia charter of April 1606 provided for the creation of a royal council to be responsible for the method of government in the new colonies and to supervise their commerce. The first settlements were governed under royal instructions, which prescribed their judicial, administrative and commercial system. Thus, though no financial responsibility was undertaken, some of the old requests of Raleigh and Hakluyt for state participation were met. The two companies were to be responsible respectively for the areas between 34° and 41° N., and 38° and 45° N, so long as they kept a neutral territory 100 miles wide between them. They were to appoint the colonial officials, who were to administer the instructions of the council of Virginia. Both companies proceeded to establish terminable joint stocks to finance the expeditions.

The Plymouth company got under way first. Pring made a voyage of reconnaissance to New England, and returned early in 1607. An expedition was sent out to the coast of Maine, and in August a site selected for Fort St. George on the Sahadahoc (now Kennebec) River. The colonists intended to establish a permanent trading-post rather than a colony of settlement. They sent the ships home with goods they collected or traded from the Indians. Raleigh Gilbert took over the presidency of the little fort early in 1608, and though food ran short the colony survived until a supply arrived in the spring. Yet failure to find minerals, quarrels among the personnel and the colonists' unwillingness to grow foodstuffs led them to desert the fort with the last ship going home in the autumn. This venture proved disappointing and the Plymouth group took no further independent action until 1620. Sir Humphrey Gilbert's chosen sphere required a different type of colonist—one prepared to re-create another England in America and to work hard in a family unit inside a closely-knit society. The Pilgrims, who founded Plymouth Colony in

1620, were the first of a series of such communities, who eventually made New England.

The London company dispensed with a reconnaissance voyage, and at the end of 1606 despatched Captain Christopher Newport and Captain Gosnold to take out the first colony. They were bound for the Chesapeake by the customary route, and they sailed past Cape Henry and the district explored by Lane's men and chose a site on a peninsula thirty miles up the James River, where they landed on May 13, 1607. Their instructions bear the impress of Hakluyt's ideas, and might have been those which Lane would have advocated in 1586. Their town must be on a navigable river, fairly far up-stream though accessible by a fifty-ton vessel, and it must have a healthy site. A small outpost should be left at the sea side. The thirteen counsellors who were to appoint their president were named in scaled instructions, and they were to put in hand the building of the fort. One-third of the company was to be employed to plant corn and other crops, thus avoiding the danger of complete dependence on the Indians, though food was to be bought from them if they would sell. Newport and Gosnold were to take an exploring party up-stream to search for a possible passage through the mainland and to hunt for minerals. The Indians were to be treated well but with great caution. Many small points show the kind of lessons that had

231

been drawn from Lane's experiences. For example, no one was to be allowed to write home anything that might discourage others. Food, stores and products grown or acquired by trade were to be managed for the benefit of the community and the company at home.

James Fort (later Jamestown) was established on an unhealthy site, which was to cost the colony dear. Newport went up the river as far as he could, but found nothing to excite hopes of a passage or of gold, though he made contacts with the powerful Powhatan confederacy of Indian tribes. He left for England in the middle of June. In the Tower at this time Raleigh's main concern was Guiana, but he kept himself informed of what was going forward in Virginia. During the summer he suggested to Salisbury that 'the journey may go under the colour of Virginia, for Newport will shortly return.' When he did he had left less than 100 men behind. Some had been lost already in an Indian attack. Food-deficiency diseases, with dysentery and malaria were all taking a terrible toll of the Jamestown settlers. Yet, though they quarrelled over leadership they got their outworks constructed and their storehouse, church and dwellings built; they raised some wheat and vegetables. Captain John Smith played an important part in organizing the constructive activities of the settlers. On an expedition he was captured by Powhatan's men, but was saved from execution by the chief's daughter, Pocahontas, and succeeded in winning their friendship and getting some extra food for the colony.

Thus the new Virginia colony, established in the region to which White's colonists of 1587 had been directed by Raleigh, survived its first winter. A sign of the new strength behind the organization at home was the early arrival of reinforcements and supplies in January 1608 and more in October. Skilled artisans and two women were among the new settlers, and a cargo of pitch, tar, glass and potash made in the colony reached England in February 1609 as an earnest of returns that might be expected from America. John Smith, as president, held the colony together between September 1608 and July 1609. It was not easy. The colonists were still like a garrison of soldiers, with little enthusiasm or initiative. Powhatan proved treacherous and remained a danger. Somehow, a harvest was reaped and the animals brought out from England were tended and made to multiply. The settlement was extended to provide dwellings for the newcomers. The shores of Chesapeake Bay, to the north of the James River estuary, were explored. But not all Smith's energy could make the colony safely self-supporting or productive. A much larger and more diversified community was needed if American soil was ever to be effectively exploited and if the English investors were to expect profits.

233

This was appreciated by the organizers of the London company, and during the winter and spring of 1608–9 intensive efforts were made to draw in new supporters and capital and to re-plan the development of the colony. Wide printed and oral publicity, in which clergymen were employed to preach sermons on the duty of going to the New World, was launched. Sub-scriptions from the city companies were col-lected, and a large number of individual sub-scribers, including many members of the Ply-mouth Company, obtained. The plan was for a terminable joint-stock to last seven years. Shares were for £12 10s., and every person who went to Virginia on his own account was credited with at least one share. At the end of the period all subscribers and settlers were to be paid off in Virginian land. Thus there was a partial rever-sion to the system which Gilbert had envisaged and to that planned by Raleigh for White's colonists in 1587. In particular, it was appre-ciated that the new colony must grow into a diversified, self-supporting and self-perpetuating community.

The council of Virginia searched widely for advice on rehabilitation. Thomas Hariot was brought before them, and asked to tell of the experiences of Lane's colony which might be helpful in the reconstruction. Raleigh, whether asked or uninvited, supplied his views on what should be done. His intervention is known only from a letter to Philip III from Don Pedro de Zuñiga, Spanish ambassador in London, dated July 5, 1609, at a time when a new supply for Virginia was on its way. Zuñiga clearly believed that Raleigh's advice was important and that it was being taken. He said:

'I have a paper which Walter Raleigh wrote, who is a prisoner in the Tower, and it is he who discovered that land and whom they consider here a very great personage. The members of the council of Virginia follow this paper; it ought to be translated because it is the original which he had and when it is finished we shall compare it with the chart which they have caused to be made, and by it, the way which they will take will be understood; where they are fortifying themselves and all the rest that your majesty commands to be known.'

This, the last known link between Raleigh and the planning of Virginia colonies, marks the end of a connexion which had lasted over thirty years. At the same time, Richard Hakluyt made his last published contribution to early colonizing literature—a translation of De Soto's travels in the North American interior. In his introduction he makes a last bid to define a native policy for the settlers:

'To handle them gently, while gentle courses may be found to serve, it will be without comparison the best: but if gentle polish-

235

ing will not serve, then we shall not want hammerers and rough masons enough, I mean our old soldiers trained up in the Netherlands, to square and prepare them to our preachers' hands.'

This is a fair summary of native policy as preached by Hakluyt and Raleigh, and it is apposite to the relations between Englishmen and the native peoples whom they afterwards came to rule.

The Virginia company got its new charter on May 23, 1609. The royal council was dispensed with; the council and treasurer of the company were to appoint the colonial officials and instruct them; the government of the colony by thirteen wrangling councillors was altered to a powerful governor with an advisory council; a new supply with 500 colonists—and insufficient food and stores—was ready to sail under Sir Thomas Gates and Sir George Somers, whom Raleigh had expected to aid him in the Guiana enterprise of 1595. All this effort did not keep the colony from the brink of disaster. The vessel containing Somers and the other leaders was wrecked on Bermuda (an accident which led to the successful occupation of this island in the next few years); the other ships discharged their unseasoned colonists and their few stores in Virginia, and, taking Smith, who had been injured, home with them, left the settlement once more to its own devices. The settlers died off like flies and failed to develop their organization to cope with their new numbers: only sixty were left after 'the starving time' of the winter of 1609–10. Meantime Somers and his company had built pinnaces to sail to the mainland. When they arrived they found the colonists destitute and desperate. They all packed on board the small vessels and were about to sail for Newfoundland when a new fleet met them. Lord de la Warr had arrived as governor just in time to save the colony. Under his rule (1610–11) it was re-established, though mortality remained very high and the organization only partly effective. Sir Thomas Dale, who took over the government during May 1611 and retained it until 1616, put the colony under a harsh and rigid discipline, but under him its continuance was assured, though it was still some way from being a paying proposition to shareholders or settlers. Trade with the Indians was small, the exploitation of American resources was largely ineffective and the preparation of ships' stores—tar, turpentine and hemp—remained experimental. Salt manufacture was the only healthy industry. The lack of a staple export was serious. John Rolfe began the exploitation of tobacco for sale in 1612, and in 1614 its export was begun. Its attractions and profits over-rode all royal and conservative objections. Gradually it became the life-blood of the colony. Then, too, before he left, Dale began the distribution of lands to the settlers

237

in accordance with the 1609 plans, though this was not proceeded with quickly, and the settlement was expanded by the foundation of Henrico and the development of better lands for corn and cattle farther up the river. Yet only 381 settlers survived when Dale left Virginia. Some were officials, rather too many for the numbers concerned; others were farmers leasing some lands from the company but working part-time on the company's plantations; the remainder were labourers and artisans.

In the years after 1616 progress was made towards a more flexible organization. A subordinate company was floated to work the 'magazine,' that is to take responsiblity for imports and exports. It was intended to exploit the needs and produce of the new class of landowners that was springing up, as well as the company's land. Subsidiary joint-stock ventures —'particular plantations'—were also permitted to exploit certain landed estates with some measure of autonomy from company rule. By the time Raleigh went to his death in 1618, the colony had been expanded sufficiently in area to be self-supporting, though emphasis on tobacco cultivation was leading to neglect of the cultivation of essential food-supplies. The colony was also becoming so diversified that it was developing from an English company's overseas estate into a community with a political life of its own.

Between 1619 and 1622 fresh efforts were made to build up the new society, but company control was never very satisfactory and insufficient profits dried up new investments. An Indian attack wiped out several hundred colonists in 1622 and retarded, though it did not stop, development. At the end of James's reign the Crown dissolved the company and instituted a royal system of government. By that time out of some 6,000 colonists who had left England for the colony less than 1,000 were alive, but they were well established and the 'new nation' of which Raleigh had dreamed and for which he had worked was coming into existence.

Chapter Eight

Guiana Gamble

IN his *Discoverie of Guiana* Raleigh set out the prospect of the discovery of a golden, civilized empire in the Guiana highlands and of the establishment of an English tropical empire over an immense native population. Neither of these attracted nor convinced many Englishmen, yet Raleigh did lead some to push on with the exploitation of the coastlands between the Amazon and the Orinoco. His *Discoverie* provided an attractive account of conditions in this region. The popularization of tobacco in England—in which Raleigh assisted—led traders to look for exploitable sources of it. The English attempts to establish small trading and plantation settlements in the Guiana lowlands largely derived from these incentives.

In prison, during the long years from 1603 to 1616, Guiana was for Raleigh a mirage in which he saw a means to pull himself out of misery and disgrace and back to wealth and influence. His repeated attempts to urge the King to let him try to rehabilitate his reputation and fortune in South America sustained him, kept him mentally alive, and ultimately led him into that last voyage when wealth and success finally evaded him.

Raleigh's last attempt to renew the Guiana venture had been in 1598; in that year he apparently had a small vessel in Guianian waters, in order to keep his credit with the native inhabitants and probably also to do some trade. Thence, to his confinement in 1603, it is possible, though not certain, that he was maintaining touch with South America by similar methods. One of the men he left behind with the Indians in 1595, Francis Sparrey, got home in 1602 after some years' imprisonment by the Spaniards, and wrote an account of his experiences after Raleigh left him. Other English ships were visiting the coast to trade. One visitor, Captain Charles Leigh, returned in 1602 determined to establish a colony on the Wiapoco —one of the many streams flowing from the highlands. With the aid of his brothers, one of whom, Sir John, was known to Raleigh, and friends, he got up a small party of settlers and left England on March 21, 1604. His intention was to establish his men on the Wiapoco, look for gold and attempt to grow flax, cotton and sugar-cane. In fact, his men lived on the Indians, who soon grew tired of this economic burden. Disease weakened the men. Another party came out later in the year and some more exploring was done, but Leigh died on board ship when about to sail for England in 1605. The remaining colonists awaited a second supply in 1605, but the ship sailed past the river and the men were mostly lost in the West Indies. Dutch and French ships took off most of the colonists in the summer. Ten who were left raised successfully a crop of flax and tobacco, and came home in a Dutch ship the following year. Charles Leigh's brothers dropped the attempt, but it shows the kind of effort which commercial speculators were willing to make, something very much less spectacular than Raleigh's plans envisaged.

After the failure of this venture, Raleigh made his first attempt to get himself out of prison and to Guiana. James I refused to countenance any offensive action against the Spanish empire, but at this time he had no special commitments to Spain and was quite willing that Englishmen should trade, settle or look for gold in places where there were no Spanish settlements. In 1607 Raleigh took the line with Salisbury that he could find gold if he were released. A piece of stone he had by him had been assayed and promised well. He could get at the mine, which was in a mountain near a river, gold being 'found but at the root of the grass, in a broad and flat slate.' His strongest appeal was to the cupidity of James's courtiers and of the King himself, and this is what he harped on for nearly ten years until it finally brought his release. While Salisbury was interested enough to bring the matter before the Privy Council it went no further, though a ship which was said to belong to Raleigh was trading on the Wiapoco in 1608.

The venture which Robert Harcourt organized in 1609 for the settlement of Guiana also has links with Raleigh. A Catholic, Harcourt got permission to take out an expedition through Prince Henry, who was in close touch with Raleigh's schemes. Harcourt knew a good deal about Raleigh's Guiana policy, and regarded himself as his follower in trying to establish English influence in the region through friendly influence over the natives. With sixty men who intended to settle under his brother Michael, he arrived on the Wiapoco in May 1609. He took formal possession for the Crown, and informed a meeting of Indian chiefs that though Raleigh had been unable to return he had come to bring Englishmen to live among them and defend them against the Caribs and other enemies. He found along the coastlands that Raleigh's name was known and respected, and encountered a chief, called Leonard, who had been to England and knew Raleigh. His objective was to establish a trading factory as the centre for a number of small trading-posts, of which he set up five during his travels, and he hoped to monopolize the trade in sugar-canes, cotton, flax, tobacco, hardwoods and dye-stuffs, in exchange for English axes, hatchets, knives, beads, mirrors, jews'-harps and other wares desired by the natives. He explored westwards from the Wiapoco and worked up the Cayenne and Marawyne Rivers before he left in September. He searched with some scepticism for gold-bearing strata and for indications of Raleigh's Manoa but without endangering the main purpose of his expedition and also without success.

It appears certain that Michael Harcourt managed his men well and kept them healthy, and until 1612 at least his factory was maintained though Robert Harcourt failed to raise money to send out fresh shipping, and apparently did most of his trading by means of Dutch ships whose activities, with those of the French, prevented the establishment of anything like an English commercial monopoly. After the homecoming of many, if not all, of the party in 1612, Robert Harcourt issued a prospectus for a terminable joint-stock venture in Guiana, and got a royal patent empowering him to form a colony. He intended to develop his commercial factories, and to add to them plantations of tobacco and sugar worked by his company and eventually reverting to the possession of the subscribers and planters. This flotation found no support and Harcourt's venture fades out, though a few of his men may have continued to reside as traders in Guiana. This is significant, as it shows that with reasonable care and some luck there was nothing to prevent Englishmen remaining as residents in the country and keeping on friendly terms with the Indians while doing so.

Raleigh, in the meantime, had been trying, unsuccessfully, in 1609 to interest one of James's Scottish favourites, Lord Haddington, in his Guiana mine, but about the end of the same year Sir Thomas Roe, afterwards famous as a diplomatist in India, Turkey and Sweden, took up the Guiana project, probably under Raleigh's influence. Raleigh put up £600 for the cost of the expedition which Roe led to South America on February 24, 1610. Roe's objective was appreciably different from Harcourt's. It was to make a thorough search for the way to Manoa both from the Amazon, a new direction for the English seekers for El Dorado, and from the Guiana lowlands. He was also anxious to spy out the strength of the Spanish positions on Trinidad and the lower reaches of the Orinoco. Salisbury, who had been busily negotiating an *entente* with France, aimed against Spain and intended to stop Spanish interference with English shipping and maltreatment of English sailors, was apparently anxious that a real search should be made for the golden kingdom, and was also considering the possibility of aggressive action against the Spanish empire if the Franco-British alliance developed and James's prejudices could be over-come. Roe's mission indicated, therefore, that there was a prospect, though far from certain, of realizing Raleigh's anti-Spanish programme and with it his particular aim of building a tropical empire.

The expedition of 1610 worked systematically up the Amazon for some 300 miles, and made some attempts to penetrate the Guiana High-lands from the south so as to find Keymis's Lake Parima; but Roe was unable to make any very protracted journeys from the river into the highlands. While he continued to hope that Manoa lay somewhere in the plateau, he had proved it could not easily be reached from the Amazon. He then returned to the Atlantic coast and examined the rivers flowing from the high-lands. He worked up beyond the navigable limits by canoe, and found, far up the Wiapoco, a level tableland which seemed attractive. Yet, after over a year's travel, Manoa remained a will-o'-the-wisp, and Roe, whose explorations were the most extensive yet attempted by the English, passed on to Trinidad a disappointed man. Indeed, though he did not entirely give up the belief in Manoa, his reports were accepted as final proof of its non-existence or complete inaccessibility by those, like Salisbury, who had been intermittently inclined to believe the story.

At Trinidad Roe learnt something of the

activities of the Spaniards in the Orinoco Basin. Since the complete failure of de Vera's ambitious attempt at colonization, little had been done to build up Spanish power. Old Berrio had died not long after Raleigh's departure, and his son Fernando, who succeeded him, had made a few unsuccessful attempts to search for Manoa in the Upper Caroni Basin. For the most part he had been content to maintain San Thomé as a military and trading post and, in spite of prohibitions by his government, to trade with English, French and Dutch traders who came up looking for tobacco and other products. Roe, significantly, declared San Thomé to be weak and easily taken. As for Trinidad, there was much trade by the Spaniards, who had settled there in the interval, with interloping merchants, while the Spanish government carried on an intermittent but ruthless warfare against the intruders. It is clear that Roe believed an attack could usefully be delivered against the still weak Spanish power in this region. This information was important for Raleigh's later activities.

During his Amazon explorations, Roe planted some twenty men near the mouth of the river and sent out what were probably small trading expeditions from England in the two years after his return in the summer of 1611. Some of the men returned as late as 1617 with a valuable cargo of tobacco and some gold. By the foundation of Para in 1615 the Portuguese began to seal the Amazon against intruders, but it was many years before they succeeded. Between 1613 and Raleigh's expedition, there are not any further clear accounts of attempts to establish colonies on the Amazon, but English, Dutch and French commerce was continuous, and it is probable that some few small trading factories were maintained. Guiana remained an English colonial objective throughout the greater part of the seventeenth century, but only the Dutch succeeded in establishing themselves permanently. Yet English trading and colonial activity in the area is significant of the demand for tropical products at home and of the desire, however unsuccessful in the long run, to form trading and plantation settlements there. This incentive was to result after Raleigh's death in the establishment of colonies on a number of the lesser West Indian islands not occupied by the Spaniards.

After 1613 there was almost no real hope of Raleigh's major scheme for an English empire on the Orinoco being put into effect. A series of deaths—Henry IV of France, Prince Henry, Salisbury—had broken down the tentative anti-Spanish alignment. The arrival of Don Diego Sarmiento de Acuña, best known by his later title of Count Gondomar, as Spanish ambassador, and his establishment of a personal ascendancy over James I, who was trying to act as his own foreign minister, marks the beginning of a new phase in English policy. James, under his guidance, began to follow his own will-o'-the-wisp of a Spanish marriage for his heir, Prince Charles. The bait was a gilded dowry of £600,000, which would go far to pay his ever-present debts, and the prospect of an arbitral position for Great Britain in the councils of Europe. For this James allowed the subtleties of Roman and Spanish theologians to drag on and on while, in the meantime, he tied English policy firmly to the avoidance of any breach with Spain.

It was the virtual ending of the Manoa myth and the shift in English policy towards Spain which made Raleigh's subsequent schemes primarily a device to obtain gold and rendered his last voyage a comparatively unimportant episode in the history of English expansion.

During 1610 and 1611, while Roe was still in the field and the anti-Spanish party still had a chance of success, Raleigh applied to the Queen, James himself, Salisbury and the Privy Council for permission to go look for his mine. The suggestion was made that Keymis, still his friend and companion, should fetch some tangible specimens home to establish proof of the mine's existence. Raleigh reluctantly consented, but for some reason the proposal dropped. Thereafter, for four years, apart from some applications by the Huguenots for Raleigh's services, which James rejected, there was no word of his release or of any new moves in his Guiana scheme.

The appointment of Sir Ralph Winwood as Secretary of State in 1614 brought into high office a man who would listen to Raleigh. The failure of the Parliament of the same year to provide the King with supplies made the government unusually desperate for money. An anti-Spanish party was still in existence at Court. In 1615 the ignoble favourite, Robert Carr, Earl of Somerset, fell. These factors enabled Raleigh to restart his planning and to obtain conditional release on March 19, 1616, to prepare for his voyage. He went to live in a house of his own in London, subject to supervision and restrictions. Before his departure, on January 30, 1617, he was given full liberty, but he was not formally pardoned and the privy seal issued to him for his voyage on August 26, 1616, was not considered to absolve him from the penalties for treason if the Crown should demand that they be imposed. It was under these disabilities that he planned and carried out his last voyage. His commission authorized him to lead an expedition unto the south parts of America, or elsewhere within America:

> 'inhabited by heathen and savage people, to the end to discover and find out some commodities and merchandises in those countries, that be necessary and profitable for the subjects of these our kingdoms and dominions,

whereof the inhabitants there make little use or estimation; whereupon also may ensue, by trade and commerce, some propagation of the Christian faith.'

No authority was given to annex territory, but no express instructions to avoid conflict with Spain were included. He was to have power to command, govern and punish the members of his expedition, and was to pay to the Crown one-fifth of all bullion and jewels acquired as well as customs on all goods brought home.

The preparations took from March 1616 to June 1617, and they aroused wide interest at home and on the continent. The assumption by the anti-Spanish elements amongst the gentry and aristocracy that Raleigh's venture would be directed against Spain, together with his popularity, which had grown since his imprisonment, and the loyalty of his friends, combined to bring in subscriptions of £15,000. By realizing everything left to him, and almost all that his wife possessed in her own right, he put up another £15,000 himself. This was sufficient, even at the high price-level of the time, to equip a formidable fleet of fourteen vessels, a number of them heavily armed. The ship he had built for himself, the *Destiny*, was of 450 tons. About 1,000 men were mobilized to sail with him. It is not surprising that the scale of the preparations should have aroused furious speculation, since it all seemed rather elaborate for a voyage to find a gold-mine which was supposed to be in unoccupied territory. The Spaniards were specially alarmed, claimed that all Guiana was Spanish-occupied territory and, through their ambassador, put the utmost pressure on James to prevent this formidable expedition from sailing. James, exceptionally susceptible to pressure by Gondomar, agreed to announce that Raleigh should forfeit his life if he came into conflict with the Spaniards or molested their property. At a later stage he even supplied precise information on the size and composition of Raleigh's fleet and on its destination. Spain could consequently take precautions to ensure that Raleigh was met with force. A conflict was expected and as a result the repudiation of Raleigh by James. It is clear that, without knowing how much the King was giving away, Raleigh appreciated the odds that were being piled up against him. As a result, he considered diverting his expedition to assist the Duke of Savoy to capture Genoa and, when this was dropped, took up a complex negotiation with France in an attempt to insure himself against some of the many risks to which he was exposed. He had the idea of getting a French force to go ahead of him to blast the Spaniards out of the Orinoco and so allow him to follow up without conflict. He also wished to provide an entry for himself into French ports if he got involved in fighting on the Orinoco so that he would have a chance to bargain with

James about the disposal of the gold which he was certain he would bring back. It does not appear that he got any firm assurances from France, but it seems clear that he considered there was very slight chance of avoiding those hostilities against which James had pledged his life. His main gamble was that if he got the gold James would pardon his actions and that his success might stimulate hostility to Spain so as to bring the King into war and Raleigh into the long-sought position of empire-builder in Guiana.

Professor Harlow suggests[1] with a good deal of probability that James was impressed by Raleigh's arguments that the Orinoco Basin was already formally-annexed British territory and that any Spaniards found there were interlopers. He could not countenance a deliberate attack on the town of San Thomé, but if Raleigh went directly to the mine and began working it and was subsequently attacked by the Spaniards James might have backed defensive action and, if the gold was plentiful enough, have proceeded to occupy the area. If so, Raleigh's expedition remained a gamble with his life, but not at such long odds.

The crux of the matter is the belief of Raleigh and Keymis in the existence of a workable mine, though they are often so deliberately misleading that their precise meaning remains

[1] V. T. Harlow, *Ralegh's Last Voyage*, pp. 25–6, 35–44.

in some doubt. Raleigh appears to have been sure that he had discovered gold-bearing rock some three miles from the site on which San Thomé had been established, and also that he and Keymis had been assured by the Indians that Mount Iconuri, which they had seen some twenty miles down the Orinoco and some fifteen miles from the river, was auriferous. In the long years of disgrace and imprisonment hopes had grown into certainties, and in his projects Raleigh was quite willing to fuse the evidence for the two mines, such as it was, into one. His original scheme appears to have been to mask the town of San Thomé with a strong force, and then work through to the gold-bearing mountain well below the town and away from the river. He revised this on hearing that the Spaniards were entrenched along the river by ordering a closer blockade of San Thomé, but it is most unlikely that he ordered Keymis to work the nearer Caroni mine instead of the Mount Iconuri one. In any event, he had some hope that there would be sufficient dissension in San Thomé, caused by an energetic attempt by a new governor to keep the inhabitants from trading with foreigners, to prevent a serious attack on his force.

Raleigh somewhat overestimated his own staying power. He was now in his middle sixties and no longer able for hardships or fatigue. As the leader of an expedition, he was no longer the dashing captain of 1578, 1595, 1596 or 1597.

Though his company included a number of
loyal and able friends, there were very many
unreliable elements in it. A number of the
officers and sailors had volunteered only as a
pretext for piracy, which was now being officially
discouraged. The expedition lacked cohesion
and Raleigh the strength to impose effective
discipline for long. Delays used up provisions
at Plymouth; storms drove the vessels back into
Plymouth and Falmouth, and ultimately into
Cork Harbour for seven weeks. It was August
19 before he finally got clear away. His sailing
orders instructed all his ships to avoid conflict
with vessels of other nations, but as he proceeded he gave orders to stop merchant vessels,
probably to prevent any attempt to spy on his
route. From some French vessels thus impounded off Cape St. Vincent he took goods for
which he paid. Some of his captains objected to
this scrupulousness. At both Lancerota and
Grand Canary he failed to induce the Spaniards
to give him provisions and lost a few men from
landing parties, but cleared from the islands in
spite of the demands of his men for an attack.
Captain John Bailie, with the *Southampton*,
deserted ostensibly because of Raleigh's piractical
actions; in fact because they were not piratical
enough. At Gomera food and water were
obtained peacefully, and on September 21 the
ships sailed southwards. Almost immediately
fever broke out on board, and Raleigh made for

Bravo, one of the Cape Verde Islands, to obtain more provisions, but was driven off by a storm. The passage across the Atlantic was a miserable one, with men dying every day, and at the end of October Raleigh himself became seriously ill. When they anchored off the mouth of the Wiapoco on November 11 he was still prostrate. He sent a boat in to try to make contact with the chief, Leonard, who was his old friend and who had helped Harcourt, and failing to find him had the fleet sail on to Caliana (Cayenne), whose cacique, Harry, had also been in England with him during recent years. The vessels assembled in the harbour there, two pinnaces having been lost on the way, and took in water. The crews cleaned up the vessels, began preparing the boats for the Orinoco journey and tried to abate the epidemic of fever. Bad weather had made the voyage an unusually long one and Raleigh was blamed by some of his men for taking such a southerly course. By December 4 preparations were nearly complete, and Raleigh and the other sick men were beginning to pick up, so the ships moved on to the Triangle Islands in order to despatch the Orinoco expedition. By this time the Spanish precautions were becoming known, and it was feared that a fleet might arrive off the delta and chase away the larger vessels, which would have to remain on guard. The commanders of the shore party insisted that Raleigh must stay to cover their retreat, as they would not trust any of the others to do so. In any event, Raleigh was still too ill to go. The critical task of finding the mine was therefore entrusted to Laurence Keymis. Sir Warham Saintleger, designated to command the troops, was also ill and was replaced by George Raleigh, Raleigh's nephew, with his son, Walter, in command of one of the companies. Five shallow-draught vessels were to enter the river with a number of boats. There were 150 sailors and 250 soldiers, a force believed sufficient to repulse any Spaniards that might be met with, since Spanish reinforcements from New Granada and Porto Rico had not yet arrived. Raleigh had been very well received by the Indians of the Guiana lowlands and the Orinoco delta. The inhabitants of the river basin also remembered him, and it appears he sent agents among them to arouse them against Spanish rule by promises of English protection. Professor Harlow suggests[1] it would have been wise tactics to incite them to a rising in which San Thomé would have been destroyed. This would have let Raleigh out, but the danger of Spanish reinforcements arriving made independent action appear advisable.

Raleigh's formal instructions to Keymis before his departure on December 10 were to proceed to the Mount Iconuri mine after he had thrown his forces between the prospecting party and

[1] V. T. Harlow, *Ralegh's Last Voyage*, pp. 45–6.

San Thomé. The soldiers were to fight and repulse the Spaniards only if attacked. If Keymis found the mine very rich, he was to hold on; if only moderately so, he was to take 'a basket or two' to satisfy the King and come back. Keymis did not do this. Was it because of secret orders or because he took matters into his own hands?[1]

On January 2, 1618, the soldiers disembarked some three to five miles below San Thomé, while the ships went on to anchor off the town, where they were fired at by the Spaniards. The town was blockaded, and there was some expectation that the small garrison there would be rendered helpless by dissensions in the town. During the night, however, English and Spanish patrols clashed. Captain Walter Raleigh dashed forward to attack and brought the rest of the English force after him. He was killed by one of the Spanish officers, but the small garrison and the inhabitants did not put up a fight. They deserted the governor, Don Diego Palomeque de Acuña, and he was killed by the attackers while they took to the woods, leaving the English in possession of the town. The total casualties were two English and three Spaniards. The attack was premature but Keymis seems to have intended to make one, despite his orders from Raleigh. That it was a poor place and that the displaced Spaniards kept up harassing attacks

[1] Cp. V. T. Harlow, *Ralegh's Last Voyage*, pp. 67–70, and A. M. C. Latham in *Essays and Studies* (1951), p. 99.

on the English did not add to its attractions for the occupying force, but its possession did open up the way to either of the two presumed mines.

For twenty-three years Keymis had asserted that he knew where there was a mine. He had corroborated Raleigh's accounts of it. Yet when it came to the point of the whole enterprise, he did not know how to go about finding it. Clearly the topography of the country looked very different from his memory of it. It was a strange, ironical and tragic climax to the whole gold-seeking project on which Raleigh had gambled everything, for even if his ultimate objectives ranged beyond gold to a colonial empire and a war with Spain, he had no hope whatever of achieving them without the discovery of precious metals to tempt James on and to justify the immediate object of the expedition. Keymis was quite unequal to the strain which was now imposed on him. He took no immediate action, in spite of pressure from the officers. Eventually he slipped away to where he thought the mine was and brought back some ore, but when it was assayed there was no gold in it. Either Raleigh had been lucky in 1595 to pick up specimens containing some gold, or else he had been deluded by the assayers, or, most probably, Keymis had not the slightest idea of where to look. In any event, he made no further attempt to search for gold up the Caroni. To keep his men quiet, he listened to stories of gold being found some few miles farther up the Orinoco, where neither he nor Raleigh had previously been. He sent up two boats, but they ran into an outpost of the fugitive Spaniards, were ambushed and suffered a number of casualties. They came back. What he did not attempt was the expedition to Mount Iconuri. This involved a journey of two or three days, and he appears to have decided not to make the attempt in the vague fear that Spanish reinforcements might come up the Orinoco and cut him off. Yet he and George Raleigh took an exploring party up the river some three hundred miles to the junction of the Guarico with the Orinoco, making observations and trying to incite the Indians to a general rising against the Spaniards. This indicated, in spite of all the probabilities, that there was still a hope that Raleigh might get away with the capture of San Thomé, and come back with a colonizing expedition even though he brought no gold to England.

The patience of the soldiers and sailors was rapidly exhausted. Raleigh had when despatching them described them as 'scum,' an indication of his opinion of their quality, but they had not disgraced themselves and it is not at all surprising that they should have resented Keymis's ineffectiveness and weak lies. Finally, they insisted he must return, and on February 1 the force left the smouldering remains of the little town which they had just burnt. On March 2 they rejoined Raleigh.

After Keymis's departure on December 10, Raleigh had worked up to Trinidad with the remaining vessels and had anchored off Punto Gallo. He evidently considered this the most likely area in which to intercept a Spanish fleet, which if it intended to blockade the Orinoco delta would almost certainly put into Port of Spain first. He took on fruit and water, and then moved round the point towards Port of Spain in order to get pitch from the famous lake and to see whether the Spanish settlers would trade. When a boat put into the harbour she was fired on and Raleigh lost a few men who were ambushed while boiling pitch. He did not retaliate, and worked back to Punto Gallo, expecting Keymis's return. On February 1 he picked up some Indians sent by the Spaniards as spies, from whom he learnt that San Thomé had fallen and that the governor and two officers had been killed, for the loss of two English captains. It is clear that the news, especially when it was confirmed by other stories, made Raleigh very anxious, but he had no direct information until Keymis arrived on March 2 to tell him that his son was dead, San Thomé destroyed and no gold found, beyond two ingots of gold from the alluvial workings which, in fact, were all the region offered.

The news had a shattering effect on Raleigh.

His grief at the loss of his son and his bewilder-
ment at the failure to find a mine unbalanced
him. Though he made frantic efforts to pull
himself and his expedition together, he was
never again, until the last scene at his execution, to take a calm and reasoned view of his
situation. Keymis invented a story that San
Thomé had been moved downstream, and that
the Spaniards driven from it continued to bar his
progress to the mine, which he could not reach.
Raleigh told Keymis he had undone him by his
negligence, and Keymis in despair committed
suicide. The two ingots, documents taken from
San Thomé showing that some Spaniards were
working alluvial gold, and the stories told by an
Indian brought from the town kept alive his
hope that there was still a mine nearby. He
urged his men to follow him in a further effort
to find it. They would not; partly because they
were disillusioned, partly because other documents taken at San Thomé showed for certain
that large Spanish reinforcements were on their
way. He did not know what to do or where to
go next. The expedition sailed off to the Leeward Islands and there desertions began. Two
ships took to piracy off Newfoundland, one he
sent home with the least useful men. For the
rest he had one plan after another, to go to Newfoundland to clean the ships and revictual, to
return to Guiana and make a final venture himself, to seize the Plate fleet, to take prizes and

bring them into French ports—it is not possible to make out a rational set of motives in something now instinctive, irrational and desperate. His remaining companions could agree with him on no plan. The fleet broke up, with some of the ships following Wollaston and Whitney after prizes, others returning home. At the end of March the *Destiny* was left alone. She sailed towards Newfoundland and Raleigh learnt that her crew contemplated mutiny and the seizure of prizes when she arrived there. He endeavoured to alter course, but some of the men did mutiny and he had to bargain with them. He agreed to make for Ireland, disembark the mutineers there and not proceed against them, and to go himself to England. He entered Kinsale, deposited the malcontents and sailed into Plymouth on June 21 after a year's absence. He returned a ruined man, with only four months to live and with his plans for a tropical empire for Great Britain in South America finally destroyed.

At home, Gondomar had long been urging that Raleigh had committed acts of violence against the Spaniards in the Canaries, and on May 23 Captain Roger North, who had left Raleigh at the Leeward Islands, arrived to give his story of the taking of San Thomé and his opinion that the whole story of the mine had been invented by Raleigh and Keymis and that Raleigh had intended to return to France. The story as the King heard it was one of deception and treachery, and he reacted by publishing proclamations disavowing any responsibility for outrages on the Spaniards and promising to punish the guilty. Gondomar pressed James for fulfilment of his promise to hand over Raleigh to the Spanish government if he broke his engagements, and the day before Raleigh arrived in England he consented. The Spaniards were astute enough to see that this would probably strengthen the anti-Spanish movement in England, and graciously consented to let James punish Raleigh himself.

No immediate attempt was made to arrest Raleigh, and when he heard how opinion had hardened against him he considered escape to France, but instead began the journey to London. Near Ashburton, Raleigh and his wife were met by Sir Lewis Stukely, vice-admiral of Devonshire and a distant cousin, who had been ordered to arrest him and bring him to London. They turned back to Plymouth for Stukely to see to the disposal of the *Destiny's* stores and tobacco, and set out again. On the way both Stukely and a French doctor, Manourie, pretended to be Raleigh's friends, but in fact tried to trap him into admissions. At Salisbury, during a few days' respite, Raleigh hurriedly wrote his *Apology for the Voyage to Guiana*, though he did not succeed in presenting it to James, who was in the district. At Brentford French agents made contact with him, and when he arrived in London at his own house in Broad Street he was visited by the French representative in England, Le Clerc, and was again offered means of escape. He refused the overtures, but on August 9 went down the Thames to pick up a vessel which was, he believed, going to the Netherlands. Stukely, who went with him, had betrayed all to the government. At Woolwich he showed his hand and formally arrested Raleigh, who was taken to the Tower the following morning. This cat-and-mouse treatment was intended to expose Raleigh's deal with France and his intention to evade imprisonment so as to strengthen the government case against him.

James had determined he must be executed to placate Spain, but to find the procedure which would appear legal and proper was not easy. A commission of Privy Councillors, headed by Bacon, collected evidence of his activities before, during, and after his voyage, and examined him three times. Sir Thomas Wilson was installed in the Tower to worm confidences out of the prisoner. Finally, on October 18, the commissioners decided that there could be no fresh trial, as Raleigh was already under sentence for high treason. The sentence could at once be put in execution or Raleigh might first be brought before a reinforced meeting of the Privy Council to be formally charged regarding his recent actions. This would have the form of a trial with an opportunity for the defence to be heard, followed by a recommendation by the council to the King that the former sentence be carried out in view of his recent offences. James was doubtful of enough members of his full council to risk this more or less public procedure. Instead, he had Raleigh called once more before the commissioners, and after a final and private examination they informed him they were of the opinion he was guilty. On October 18 he was brought before the court of King's Bench for confirmation of the verdict of 1603. His attempt to plead an implied pardon by the issue to him of the commission of 1616 was set aside, and his execution ordered. It was fixed for the following day, the only concession being that he should die honourably by beheading instead of the hanging, drawing and quartering of the original sentence. The sentence was carried out in Old Palace Yard.

The basis of Raleigh's self-justification which he maintained consistently, though he added various true and untrue trimmings during the last stages of the process against him, was that 'these parts bordering the River Orinoco, and to the south as far as the River Amazon, doth by the law of nations belong to the Crown of England.' If Spaniards were there, they were intruders whom a loyal subject had a right to expel. He remained confident in the existence of a mine, though he did not disclose that he had gone to Guiana with two possible mines in view. He claimed that unknown to him the Spaniards had built a village, not on the original site of Morequito but so near to the mine as to make it impossible for his men to reach it without danger of conflict. This story of the moving of San Thomé was an untruth, but was intended to meet the discrepancies which his conjoint story of the two mines had laid bare. He disclaimed responsibility for the action of his subordinates in disobeying orders by coming into conflict with the Spaniards and occupying and destroying San Thomé: while at the same time he urged Spanish cruelties towards and attacks on Englishmen in many parts of America as reasons why her protests at the action of the expedition should be taken lightly. The preparations which had been made to reinforce the whole area before his arrival seemed to justify him in taking precautionary action, while he stressed his own moderation in forbearing to make any attack on Spanish shipping or on the Spanish coastal and island settlements from Trinidad westwards. There were inconsistencies and mis-statements in his arguments, but they reflect, basically, his passionate desire to justify the asertion of British sovereignty over the Orinoco Basin, and the consequent reasons for hostility towards Spain in America.

The official *Declaration*, published after his execution, reprinted Raleigh's commission and declared that in spite of it and of all royal precautions:

> '. . . it appeareth plainly, by the whole sequel of his actions, that he went his own way, and had his own ends: first, to secure his liberty, and then to make new fortunes for himself, casting abroad only this tale of the mine as a lure to get adventurers and followers, having in his eye the Mexico fleet, the sackings and spoil of towns planted with Spaniards, the depredation of ships and such other purchase; and making account, that, if he returned rich, he would ransom his offences, little looking into the nature and character of his majesty's justice and government; and, if otherwise, he would seek his fortune by flight, and new enterprises in some foreign country.'

His guilt was certain and an example must be made of him.

Raleigh made a dignified end on the scaffold, repudiating all the charges against him. The circumstances of his death greatly strengthened anti-Spanish feeling and he came to be regarded by many as a martyr, as one who had been killed by Gondomar rather than King James. To the Parliamentarians in their subsequent struggle with the Stuarts he appeared a victim of royal tyranny. His works, the *Historie of the World* in particular, became widely popular amongst the opponents of the monarchy. His independent and critical judgments on institutions and prominent men of the past, as well as his insistence that rulers must regard the law and not act as tyrants, were subversive of that blind ideological acceptance of a divinely-sponsored, absolute monarchy which the Stuarts wished to impose. Hostility to the Spanish empire in the west and a renewed English challenge to its supremacy had to await a Cromwell before they became practical politics. As the hero of the Puritans, Raleigh's influence flourished to some extent on a myth, but the many-sidedness of his character, abilities and intellect, as well as the dramatic quality of many of the incidents of his life, have given his personality a permanent interest, changing its focus and emphasis in each generation.

In the history of the formative period of English overseas expansion, Raleigh occupies an enduring place. He does so, not because of his long protagonism of English as against Spanish imperialism, nor from any lasting achievement in the establishment of English authority overseas. His contribution was made rather to English colonial theory. In the first place, he did as much as any other individual of his age to place American colonization in the public mind as a fixed and continuing objective. Only Richard Hakluyt the younger can stand at his side in this respect, and only his half-brother, Sir Humphrey Gilbert, can claim any importance among the other Elizabethan colonial enthusiasts. His experiments in North Carolina proved that, even if success was not easily achieved, North America was a rich land suitable for settlement. He advanced from the concept of a military settlement of hired men to the view that only a real community of men, women and children, having personal incentives to settle and prosper, could hope to succeed. This, though not at once acceptable in the early seventeenth century, proved to be a basis for successful English settlements in North America. In the second place, he put forward, in connexion with the Guiana venture, a theory of tropical imperialism. Most of his contemporaries regarded the Spanish empire as something to be robbed: Raleigh thought of it as something to be replaced by an English empire. He therefore considered seriously the problems of English rule over a native population, which must continue to form the bulk of the inhabitants after the conquest. He believed that by a more benevolent and constructive native policy he could make the South American Indians an instrument for the overthrow of Spanish rule, and that it would be possible to maintain good relations with the natives while exploiting their economic resources and labour and installing white colonies among them. This was not, as some have suggested, a policy of benevolent idealism but of enlightened self-interest. It took,

and could take, little account of the real problems of economic association and political
domination to which imperialism of this sort
gives rise. What he did do in this respect was to
introduce the concept of tropical imperialism
into English colonial thinking. It was scarcely
yet appropriate to the needs and capacities of a
small trading nation which was only beginning
to develop its industrial potential. His North
American plans, however, were capable of
achievement in some measure by his own
society. Under-employment at home, religious
and social dissensions, the search for profitable
investment in new fields for small and large
capitals alike, contributed the people and the
money for the pioneer settlements in Virginia
and New England. It was the social dynamics of
the England of the late Tudor and early Stuart
period which made English overseas colonization
possible, but Raleigh's ideas and experiments
helped in its realization. That is his principal
claim to an important position in the making of
an English overseas empire.

Note on Further Reading

On the overseas background J. A. Williamson, *Age of Drake* (2nd ed. 1946), A. L. Rowse, *The Expansion of Elizabethan England* (1955), and *The Elizabethans and America* (1959), are the best introductions. Of the many lives of Raleigh the more useful ones are Edward Edwards (with his letters, 2 vols. 1868), William Stebbing (2nd ed. 1899), Edward Thompson (1935), Sir Philip Magnus (1956), and W. M. Wallace (1959). E. A. Strathmann, *Sir Walter Ralegh. A Study in Elizabethan Skepticism* (1951), A. M. C. Latham, 'Sir Walter Ralegh's gold mine', in *Essays and Studies by Members of the English Association* (1951), and Walter Oakeshott, *The Queen and the Poet* (1960), deal with particular aspects of his life.

The documents on Raleigh's overseas ventures may be found in *The Voyages and Colonising Enterprises of Sir Humphrey Gilbert* (2 vols. 1940) and *The Roanoke Voyages, 1584–90* (2 vols. 1955), both collections edited by D. B. Quinn; *The Discoverie of Guiana* (1928) and *Ralegh's Last Voyage* (1932), both edited by V. T. Harlow. Many are also in Richard Hakluyt, *The Principal Navigations* (12 vols. 1903–4; Everyman edition, 8 vols.). Samples from *The Historie of the World* (1614) are in Sir Walter Ralegh, *Selections from his Writings*, edited by G. E. Hadow (1917); it appears in full in his *Works* (8 vols. 1829), the last volume containing his miscellaneous writings. Miss A. M. C. Latham's edition of his *Poems* (2nd edition, 1951) is the best.

Index

273

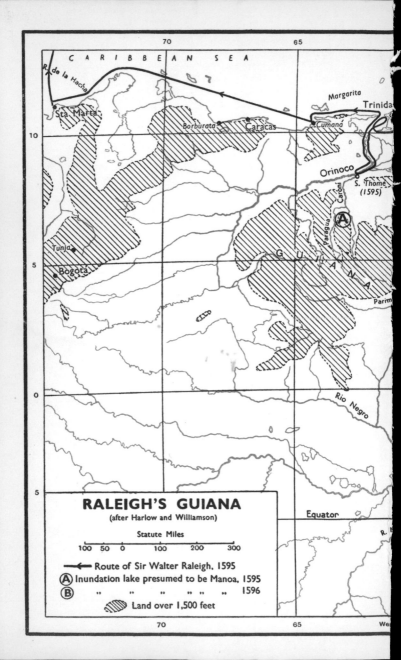

RALEIGH'S GUIANA
(after Harlow and Williamson)

Statute Miles

100 50 0   100   200   300

⟵ Route of Sir Walter Raleigh, 1595
Ⓐ Inundation lake presumed to be Manoa, 1595
Ⓑ   "   "   "   "   "   "   1596
▨ Land over 1,500 feet